The Role of Axiomatics and Problem Solving in Mathematics

■ *The Conference Board*
of the Mathematical Sciences
WASHINGTON, D.C.

GINN AND COMPANY

PREFACE

For the International Congress of Mathematicians, scheduled for the summer of 1966 in Moscow, U.S.S.R., the International Commission on Mathematical Instruction chose three topics as being of particular interest at the time. These three topics were:

A. University programs in mathematics for physicists;

B. The use of the axiomatic method in the teaching of mathematics in the secondary school;

C. The role of problems in the development of mathematical activity in students.

The national commission of each of the countries adhering to the International Commission on Mathematical Instruction was asked to report on the state of affairs in its country with respect to each of these three topics. When this charge was discussed by the United States Commission on Mathematical Instruction,* it was agreed that the first topic had already been thoroughly studied by the Panel on Physical Sciences and Engineering of the Committee on the Undergraduate Program in Mathematics. On the other hand, it was agreed that there is a wide diversity of opinion in this country with respect to the other two topics, in particular that concerning the axiomatic method.

The United States Commission felt that any report to the International Commission should reflect this wide range of opinions and that an effective way of doing this would be to ask individual mathematicians and mathematics teachers, representing various points of view, to prepare statements of their own opinions on these matters.

The United States Commission felt that the set of these statements could not only form the report to the International Commission but also, if made widely available in the United States, encourage discussion of these important topics and, hopefully, reduce misunderstandings in the mathematical community.

The Conference Board of the Mathematical Sciences was asked to undertake the solicitation of these statements and to arrange for their publication. A grant from the National Science Foundation provided the necessary financial support. The undersigned, a member-at-large of the Conference Board, was asked to oversee the work.

It is the sincere hope of both the United States Commission on Mathematical Instruction and the Conference Board of the Mathematical Sciences that the clear expression of various points of view on these two aspects of mathematics education to be found in this booklet will contribute to the improvement of mathematics education in this country and elsewhere.

E. G. Begle

---

* Members of USCMI were E. G. Begle, Stanford University; R. C. Buck, University of Wisconsin; Burton Jones, University of Colorado; P. S. Jones, University of Michigan; H. O. Pollak, Bell Telephone Laboratories; and R. J. Walker, Cornell University.

CONTENTS

■ *Frank B. Allen*

THE USE OF THE AXIOMATIC METHOD
IN TEACHING HIGH SCHOOL MATHEMATICS

The axiomatic method is concerned with *proof* in school mathematics. It is a *method of exposition* which furnishes a foundation for proof as well as the principles needed for constructing proofs and for testing the validity of arguments. The foundation is provided by stressing the importance of carefully stated assumptions, properties, and definitions. The principles consist of such rudiments of logic as the transitive property of implication. Indeed these rudiments of logic, being common to all sciences, are more appropriately described as axioms than, say, the properties of an ordered field, which are peculiar to mathematics.

The axiomatic method gives the student something to reason *from* and something to reason *with*. It requires that both teacher and pupil play the game of "How do we know?" according to rules that are known to both. This may make the game more difficult—particularly for the teacher. In the long run, however, it makes the game far more interesting and instructive than it was when only the teacher knew the rules—if there were any. Played by stated rules the game of "How do we know?" is a game that everybody wins.

Some pupils who have studied the axiomatic method would understand, appreciate, and hopefully, be able to construct "flow-diagram" proofs such as those shown below. As a first step toward understanding the proofs, they would supply the reasons for each of the numbered implications.

A. $x \in R \xrightarrow{(1)} |x| = \sqrt{x^2} \xrightarrow{(2)} |x| = \sqrt{(-x)^2} \xrightarrow{(3)} |x| = |-x|$
$$\therefore x \in R \xrightarrow{(4)} |x| = |-x|$$

B. $x \in R \xrightarrow{(1)} \left\{ \begin{array}{l} x^2 \geqslant 0 \xrightarrow{(2)} |x^2| = x^2 \\ \\ and \\ \\ |x| = \sqrt{x^2} \xrightarrow{(3)} |x|^2 = x^2 \end{array} \right\} \xrightarrow{(4)} |x^2| = |x|^2$

$$\therefore x \in R \xrightarrow{(5)} |x^2| = |x|^2$$

1

$$C.\ x \in R \xrightarrow{(1)} \begin{cases} x \geqslant 0 \xrightarrow{\quad(2)\quad} x = |x| \\ \qquad\qquad\qquad \begin{cases} \xrightarrow{(3)} x \leqslant |x| \\ \xrightarrow{(5)} x \geqslant -|x| \end{cases} \xrightarrow{(6)} -|x| \leqslant x \leqslant |x|. \\[4pt] or \xrightarrow{\quad(4)\quad} |x| \geqslant -|x| \\[6pt] x < 0 \xrightarrow{(7)} |x| = -x \xrightarrow{(8)} -|x| = x \begin{cases} \xrightarrow{(10)} |x| \geqslant x \\ \xrightarrow{(9)} -|x| \leqslant x \end{cases} \xrightarrow{(11)} -|x| \leqslant |x|. \end{cases}$$

$$\therefore x \in R \xrightarrow{(12)} -|x| \leqslant x \leqslant |x|$$

An analysis of these proofs will show that the reason for the last step in each is the transitive property of implication. The reason for step (3) in the third proof is a theorem in logic, namely, $a \longrightarrow (a \vee b)$. The same reason supports step (9).

The flow-diagram arrangement presents an argument in a form where merciless analysis is facilitated. We are not, at this point, concerned with such analyses. These proofs are important only because they illustrate a relatively new phenomenon in school mathematics—*proof in algebra.*

Most of the algebra texts published in the United States since 1960 delineate the structure of algebra by presenting the properties of an ordered field as a basis for justifying statements which, in former years, would have merely been announced as rules for computation. Some of these books have sections on logic which give the student an idea of the nature of proof. A few texts present logic as an integral part of the course and use it throughout in the proof of theorems. In some cases, the proofs are short, informal essays designed to convince the student that a certain proposition is true. Sometimes proofs are structured in ledger form, as they are in traditional geometry texts, with the reasons numbered to correspond to the steps. In a few books we find "flow-diagram" proofs of the kind shown above.

The prevalence of these patterns of proof in commercially produced texts indicates that publishers now believe that there is a substantial demand for texts that emphasize structure and proof in algebra.

This belief is amply vindicated by an examination of the courses of study which fifty high schools have submitted with their applications for membership in Mu Alpha Theta since September 1965. Since Mu Alpha Theta is a national organization of high school and junior college mathematics clubs sponsored by the Mathematical Association of America, we must concede that the schools which apply for membership form a somewhat select group. Nevertheless the contrast between current programs in these schools and the programs found in most high schools ten years ago is striking and highly significant. One recent application, typical of many received, lists "logic" and "a closer look at proof" in its tenth-grade program and "Statements and Sets," "Ordered Fields," "Mathematical Induction—Sequence and Series," "The

Algebra of Vectors," "Functions," and the "Field of Complex Numbers" in its twelfth-grade sequence. Nearly all of these fifty schools describe programs in which the structure of algebra and the nature of algebraic proof are stressed. This emphasis on structure and proof in algebra is the fundamental component of a change that has taken place in school mathematics in the United States at the secondary level during the last ten years. This change is so profound and far reaching that it can only be described as a *revolution*.

The writer is among the many teachers of high school mathematics who welcome this revolution. We believe that the axiomatic method of exposition will help pupils acquire a deeper understanding of elementary mathematics and a better appreciation of the nature of mathematics. While we are aware that a vocal minority of mathematicians have expressed dismay with this method by denouncing "excessive formality," "trivial proofs," "logical gems," and "long lists of properties," our confidence in the method is, we believe, endorsed by the majority of mathematicians who have contributed to the improvement of school mathematics during the last decade by participating in the various writing groups. Most important of all, this confidence is sustained by our daily experiences in the classroom.

The purpose of this paper is to show, by examples chosen from classroom notes, why many teachers believe that the axiomatic method helps the student to acquire a better understanding of the nature of proof. In order to do this, it is necessary to "lay out our tools" by indicating the rudiments of logic which are available for use. These are indicated in a general way in the following paragraphs. In each case the numeral at the right indicates the grade level at which the topic is studied.

The essentials of logic include the concept that a statement is a sentence the truth value of which, can be assigned, that is, a sentence which is either true or false. In addition, the student must understand each of the following:

1. The statement that statements p and q are equivalent is written $p \longleftrightarrow q$. (9)
   This statement is true if p and q are both true or both false and false otherwise.
   For example, if A and B represent sets, we have (Some members of A are members of B) $\longleftrightarrow A \cap B \neq \emptyset$.
2. The conjunction of statements p and q is written $p \wedge q$. This state- (9) ment is true if both p and q are true and false otherwise.
3. The disjunction of statements p and q is written $p \vee q$. This state- (9) ment is false when both p and q are false and true otherwise.
4. The implication "If p then q" is expressed symbolically as $p \longrightarrow q$. (9)
   This statement is true unless q is false when p is true. Statement p is the hypothesis of this implication and statement q is its conclusion.
5. A contradiction of the statement p is written $\longrightarrow p$ and is true when (9) p is false and false when p is true.
   For example, a contradiction of $A \cap B \neq \emptyset$ is $A \cap B = \emptyset$.

3

Thus $\sim$ (Some members of A are members of B) $\longleftrightarrow$ (No members of A are members of B).

6. (a) $\sim (p \wedge q) \longleftrightarrow (\sim p \vee \sim q)$.
   (b) $\sim (p \vee q) \longleftrightarrow (\sim p \wedge \sim q)$.

7. $\sim (p \longrightarrow q) \longleftrightarrow (p \wedge \sim q)$. (9)

8. Each implication $p \longrightarrow q$ has certain other implications related to it. (9)
   These are
   (a) the converse, $q \longrightarrow p$,
   (b) the inverse, $\sim p \longrightarrow \sim q$, and
   (c) the contrapositive, $\sim q \longrightarrow \sim p$.
   Of (a)—(c) only the contrapositive is equivalent to the original implication. Thus we have $(p \longrightarrow q) \longleftrightarrow (\sim q \longrightarrow \sim p)$.

9. In the implication $p \longrightarrow q$, p may be a conjunctive statement such as $(a \wedge b \wedge c)$. In this case $(a \wedge b \wedge c) \longrightarrow q$ has a complete converse $q \longrightarrow (a \wedge b \wedge c)$, for which we have little use, and three partial converses $(q \wedge b \wedge c) \longrightarrow a$, $(a \wedge q \wedge c) \longrightarrow b$ and $(a \wedge b \wedge q) \longrightarrow c$. (10–11)
   If both the hypothesis and conclusion are conjunctive statements, we may form partial converses by exchanging any number of clauses in the conclusion with a like number of clauses in the hypothesis. Thus a theorem having the form $(a \wedge b) \longrightarrow (x \wedge y \wedge z \wedge w)$ has 14 partial converse forms such as $(x \wedge y) \longrightarrow (a \wedge b \wedge z \wedge w)$ and $(a \wedge y) \longrightarrow (x \wedge b \wedge z \wedge w)$.

10. The implication $(a \wedge b \wedge c) \longrightarrow q$ has a complete contrapositive $\sim q \longrightarrow \sim (a \wedge b \wedge c)$, for which we have little use, and three partial contrapositives $(\sim q \wedge b \wedge c) \longrightarrow \sim a$, $(a \wedge \sim q \wedge c) \longrightarrow \sim b$ and $(a \wedge b \wedge \sim q) \longrightarrow \sim c$. All of these contrapositives are equivalent to the original implication. This fact often suggests several different attacks on the problem of proving a given theorem. (10)

11. A tautology is a compound statement which is true regardless of the truth or falsity of its component statements. Examples: (10)
    (a) $a \vee \sim a$
    (b) $(p \wedge p \rightarrow q) \rightarrow q$
    (c) $(p \longrightarrow q \wedge q \longrightarrow r) \longrightarrow (p \longrightarrow r)$ or, more briefly, $(p \longrightarrow q \longrightarrow r) \longrightarrow (p \longrightarrow r)$
    (d) $(\sim t \wedge \sim q \longrightarrow t) \longrightarrow q$

12. (a) An argument is an assertion that a certain statement, called the conclusion of the argument, is true when certain other statements, called the premises of the argument, are true. (10–11)
    (b) An argument is *valid* if the implication which has the premises of the argument for its hypothesis and the conclusion of the argument for its conclusion is a tautology. (10–11)
    (c) A proof is a valid argument having true premises. (10–11)

Each of the following tautologies becomes a proof of its conclusion if we know that each statement in its hypothesis is true.

$$(i) \; [p \wedge (p \longrightarrow q)] \longrightarrow q$$
$$(ii) \; [(p \longrightarrow q) \wedge (q \longrightarrow r)] \longrightarrow (p \longrightarrow r)$$

4

(iii) $[\sim t \wedge (\sim q \longrightarrow t)] \longrightarrow q$

(iv) $[p \longrightarrow (a \wedge b) \wedge (a \longrightarrow x) \wedge (b \longrightarrow y) \wedge (x \wedge y) \longrightarrow z] \longrightarrow (p \longrightarrow z)$

(v) $[p \longrightarrow (a \vee b) \wedge (a \to x) \wedge (b \to x)] \to (p \to x)$

(vi) $[(r \vee s) \wedge (r \vee t) \wedge \sim (s \wedge t)] \longrightarrow r$

(vii) $[(a \underline{\vee} b \underline{\vee} c) \wedge (a \longrightarrow x) \wedge (b \longrightarrow y) \wedge (c \longrightarrow z) \wedge (x \underline{\vee} y \underline{\vee} z)] \longrightarrow$
$\qquad\qquad\qquad\qquad [(x \longrightarrow a) \wedge (y \longrightarrow b) \wedge (z \longrightarrow c)]$

In statement (vii) the symbol $\underline{\vee}$ represents the "exclusive or," so that "$a \underline{\vee} b \underline{\vee} c$" can be read "$a$ or else b or else c" and is true when exactly one of these statements is true and false otherwise. The statement (vii) is sometimes referred to as the *Law of Converses*.

With these principles of logic available and assuming knowledge of the properties of an ordered field, the properties of equality and a reasonable facility with the language of sets, including the set-builder notation, we consider some classroom situations.

1. We wish to solve the equation
   $5 + \sqrt{n + 7} = n$, $n \epsilon R$ (n is a real number).
   Discussion: The students know that in solving equations, we sometimes obtain "extraneous roots," that is, roots of derived equations that do not satisfy the original equation. The axiomatic method helps to explain why this is so.

   Suppose a is a number which satisfies the given equation. Then $5 + \sqrt{a + 7}$ $= a \longrightarrow \sqrt{a + 7} = a - 5 \longrightarrow a + 7 = a^2 - 10a + 25 \longrightarrow a^2 - 11a + 18$ $= 0 \longrightarrow (a - 9)(a - 2) = 0 \longrightarrow a - 9 = 0 \vee a - 2 = 0 \longrightarrow a = 9 \vee a = 2$.
   We have shown that if a is a member of the solution set of the given equation then $a \epsilon \{2,9\}$. Since the converse of a, a true implication, is not necessarily true, there is no reason to suppose that any member of $\{2,9\}$ will satisfy our equation. We know only that $\{n | 5 + \sqrt{n + 7} = n\} \subseteq \{2,9\}$. A check reveals that 9 is in our solution set and 2 is not.

2. We have had the theorem $ab = 0 \longrightarrow (a = 0 \vee b = 0)$. We ask the students to explain why the equation $(x - 7)(x - 2) = 0$ can have no roots other than 2 and 7.

   Unless the students understand how to contradict a disjunctive statement and the principle of the contrapositive 8(c), they will fail to see that the conclusion follows directly from the theorem. Thus, if $x \notin \{7,2\}$, then $x - 7 \neq 0 \wedge x - 2$ $\neq 0$ and hence $(x - 7)(x - 2) \neq 0$ because $(a \neq 0 \wedge b \neq 0) \longrightarrow (ab \neq 0)$.

3. What is involved in proving a theorem, such as the following, whose statement contains the phrase "if and only if"?

   Theorem: Real numbers r and s are roots of the equation $x^2 + px + q = 0$ if and only if $r + s = -p$ and $rs = q$. First we note that this theorem can be stated as follows: For r, $s \epsilon R$, (r and s are roots of $x^2 + px + q = 0$) $\longleftrightarrow$ ($r + s$ $= -p$ and $rs = q$). Now $(a \longleftrightarrow b) \longleftrightarrow [(a \longrightarrow b) \wedge (b \longrightarrow a)]$. Thus to prove an "if and only if" theorem, we must prove the *left to right* implication and the *right to left* implication. Classroom experience tells us that students need a

5

great deal of reminding on this point. The proof of the left to right part of this theorem follows immediately from the fact that the roots of the given equation are $\dfrac{-p + \sqrt{p^2 - 4q}}{2}$ and $\dfrac{-p - \sqrt{p^2 - 4q}}{2}$.

The proof of the right to left part
$$[(r + s = -p) \wedge (rs = q)] \longrightarrow (r \text{ and } s \text{ are roots of } x^2 + px + q = 0)$$
can be arranged as follows:
$$r + s \overset{(1)}{=} -p \overset{(2)}{\longrightarrow} \left.\begin{matrix} r = -p - s \\ rs \overset{(3)}{=} q \end{matrix}\right\} \overset{(4)}{\longrightarrow} (-p - s)s = q \overset{(5)}{\longrightarrow} -ps - s^2 = q$$
$$\overset{(6)}{\longrightarrow} s^2 + ps + q = 0 \overset{(7)}{\longrightarrow} s \text{ is a root of } x^2 + px + q = 0.$$
Similarly we can show that r is a root of $x^2 + px + q = 0$.

If the conclusion of a theorem is a statement of equivalence, then the implication may have the form $(a \wedge b) \longrightarrow (x \longleftrightarrow y)$. This theorem can be proved by proving two implications: $(a \wedge b \wedge x) \longrightarrow y$ and $(a \wedge b \wedge y) \longrightarrow x$. If we agree to write $a \wedge b \wedge c$ in the "vertical form" that facilitates the writing of flow-diagram proofs, then

$$\left[\left.\begin{matrix} a \\ b \\ x \end{matrix}\right\} \longrightarrow y \wedge \left.\begin{matrix} a \\ b \\ y \end{matrix}\right\} \longrightarrow x \right] \longrightarrow \left[\left.\begin{matrix} a \\ b \end{matrix}\right\} \longrightarrow (x \longleftrightarrow y) \right]$$

is a tautology as can be shown by a 16-line truth table.

This pattern of proof is used in proving such theorems as:
"If $a > 0 \wedge b > 0$, then $(a > b) \longleftrightarrow (a^2 > b^2)$,"
"If $a < 0$, then $(b > c) \longleftrightarrow (ab < ac)$,"
"If $x, a \epsilon R$ and $a \geqslant 0$, then $(|x| \leqslant a) \longleftrightarrow (-a \leqslant x \leqslant a)$."

"If L_1 and L_2 are distinct nonvertical lines, L_1 is the graph of $\{(x,y) \mid y = m_1 x + k_1\}$, and
L_2 is the graph of $\{(x,y) \mid y = m_2 x + k_2\}$, then
$L_1 \| L_2$ if and only if $m_1 = m_2$ and $k_1 \neq k_2$."

There are many other theorems of this type.

4. We have proved theorem X, "The number t is an odd integer if and only if $t = 2k + 1$ where k is an integer," and we are considering theorem Y, "If a^2 is an even integer, then a is an even integer." How can we proceed?

If a is an integer $(a \epsilon I)$, the statements "a^2 is not an even integer" and "a^2 is an odd integer" are equivalent, and the statements "a is not an even integer" and "a is an odd integer" are equivalent. Therefore theorem Y can be established by proving its contrapositive, namely, "If a is an odd integer, then a^2 is an odd integer." This proof can be presented as follows: a is an odd integer $\overset{(1)}{\longrightarrow} a^2 = (2k + 1)^2 \overset{(2)}{\longrightarrow} a^2 = 4k^2 + 4k + 1 \overset{(3)}{\longrightarrow} a^2 = 2(2k^2 + 2k) + 1 \overset{(4)}{\longrightarrow} a^2 = 2k + 1 \wedge k \epsilon I \overset{(5)}{\longrightarrow} a^2$ is an odd integer.

Another example of the use of the contrapositive is the proof of the statement:
If $a > 0$, then $[(x - a)(x + a) < 0] \longrightarrow [(x + a > 0) \wedge (x - a < 0)]$.
In our preliminary discussion we note that $x - a$ and $x + a$ must be opposite

in sign since their product is negative. Then $x + a$ must be positive. If it were negative, then $x - a$ would also be negative because, with $a > 0$, $x + a > x - a$ and the signs of $x + a$ and $x - a$ would be the same. Since $x + a > 0$, we must have $x - a < 0$ in order for the signs of these expressions to be opposite. Now the students "see" that the theorem is true. They have a partial answer to the persistent question, "How do we know?" All this is a necessary prerequisite to the construction of a flow-diagram proof which is the acid test of understanding. Many times we have thought we understood a theorem only to find that we had made an unwarranted assumption which did not show up until a flow-diagram proof was attempted.

In this case we break our statement into parts s and t as follows:

$$s: \quad \left.\begin{array}{c} a > 0 \\ (x - a)(x + a) < 0 \end{array}\right\} \longrightarrow x - a < 0 \quad \text{and}$$

$$t: \quad \left.\begin{array}{c} a > 0 \\ (x - a)(x + a) < 0 \end{array}\right\} \longrightarrow x + a > 0.$$

Statement s is readily established by proving the contrapositive.

$$\left.\begin{array}{c} a > 0 \\ x - a \geqslant 0 \end{array}\right\} \longrightarrow (x - a)(x + a) \geqslant 0.$$

Proof:

$$s: \quad \left.\begin{array}{c} a > 0 \xrightarrow{(1)} 2a > 0 \\ x - a \geqslant 0 \end{array}\right\} \longrightarrow \left.\begin{array}{c} x + a > 0 \\ x - a \geqslant 0 \end{array}\right\} \longrightarrow (x + a)(x - a) \geqslant 0$$

We omit the proof of t which is quite similar.

5. For every positive number a and for every counting number n we have proved the following:
   1. $0 < a < 1 \longrightarrow 0 < a^n < 1$
   2. $a = 1 \longrightarrow a^n = 1$
   3. $a > 1 \longrightarrow a^n > 1$.
   Now we are asked to prove the statement, "If a is a positive number and n is a counting number, then $a_n > 1 \longrightarrow a > 1$."
   For a positive, we have $(0 < a < 1 \vee a = 1 \vee a > 1)$ and $(0 < a^n < 1 \vee a^n = 1 \vee a^n > 1)$ by the trichotomy property. Therefore the Law of Converses (vii) applies, and we know at once that the following three converses are true:
   1′. $0 < a^n < 1 \longrightarrow 0 < a < 1$
   2′. $a^n = 1 \longrightarrow a = 1$
   3′. $a^n > 1 \longrightarrow a > 1$
   There are many applications for the Law of Converses in both algebra and geometry.

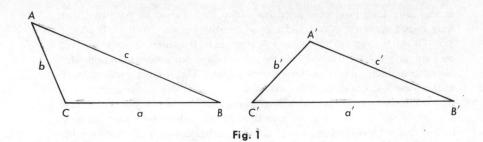

Fig. 1

Let ABC and $A'B'C'$ (Fig. 1) be triangles and suppose we have proved that for $a = a'$, $b = b'$, and $(m \angle C > m \angle C' \longrightarrow c > c')$. Also suppose that we have proved the S.A.S. congruence theorem. Then the stage is set for the proof of $(c > c' \longrightarrow m \angle C > m \angle C')$ using the Law of Converses because we have:

$$m \angle C > m \angle C' \longrightarrow c > c',$$
$$m \angle C = m \angle C' \longrightarrow c = c',$$
$$m \angle C < m \angle C' \longrightarrow c < c'.$$

For distinct collinear points A, B, and C, we can show that:

(1) A between B and $C \longrightarrow (BC > AB \wedge BC > AC)$ (1)′
(2) B between A and $C \longrightarrow (AC > AB \wedge AC > BC)$ (2)′
(3) C between A and $B \longrightarrow (AB > AC \wedge AB > BC)$ (3)′

($|AB|$ represents the measure of line segment AB.)

We can also prove that each of the statements, (1) $\vee$ (2) $\vee$ (3) and (1′) $\vee$ (2′) $\vee$ (3′) is true. Therefore the Law of Converses enables us to prove the following lemma:

If A, B, and C are distinct collinear points and $|AB| > |AC| \wedge |AB| > |BC|$, then C is between A and B.

This lemma is useful, in fact, indispensable, in proving Theorem 6–20 in the SMSG text, *Geometry with Coordinates*, which can be stated as follows:

If, in $\triangle ABC$, $|AB| > |AC|$, $|AB| > |BC|$, and the perpendicular to $\overleftrightarrow{AB}$ through C intersects $\overleftrightarrow{AB}$ in point X, then X is between A and B. (This theorem is used in the proof of the Pythagorean Theorem.)

Other applications of the Law of Converses are suggested by the drawing below.

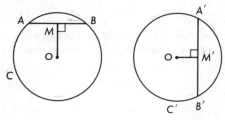

Fig. 2

If in congruent circles C and C' (Fig. 2) we have proved that $|OM| = |O'M'|$ $\longrightarrow |AB| = |A'B'|$ and $|OM| > |O'M'| \longrightarrow |AB| < |A'B'|$, then we know that $|OM| < |O'M'| \longrightarrow |AB| > |A'B'|$, and we can immediately establish the converses of these three statements by the Law of Converses.

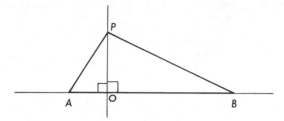

Fig. 3

Similarly if we have proved that $|AO| < |OB| \longrightarrow |AP| < |PB|$ and $|AO| = |OB| \longrightarrow |AP| = |PB|$ (See Fig. 3), we can quickly prove the converses of these statements by the Law of Converses without appealing to the Pythagorean Theorem.

6. We wish to prove the following theorem:

   If L_1 is the graph of $\{(x, y) \mid y = mx + k_1\}$ and L_2 is the graph of $\{(x, y) \mid y = mx + k_2\}$ and $k_1 \neq k_2$, then $L_1 \parallel L_2$.

   In this situation we would accept an indirect essay proof such as the following:

   If L_1 is not parallel to L_2, then L_1 and L_2 must have at least one point $P(a, b)$ in common. In this case $b = ma + k_1$ and $b = ma + k_2$ and this implies that $k_1 = k_2$. However $k_1 \neq k_2$. We conclude that $L_1 \parallel L_2$ because $[(k_1 \neq k_2) \wedge (L_1$ is not parallel to $L_2 \longrightarrow k_1 = k_2)] \longrightarrow L_1 \parallel L_2$ by 11 (d) on page 4.

   Indirect proof holds no terrors for pupils who are acquainted with the contrapositive principle. Instead of using 11 (d), many of my students would "shift to the contrapositive" and prove that, under the conditions of the theorem, $(L_1$ is not parallel to $L_2) \longrightarrow k_1 = k_2$. Then they would establish the truth of the original theorem by invoking the contrapositive principle.

7. We are to prove the "Coordinate Systems Theorem" which is stated as follows in the SMSG text, *Geometry with Coordinates*. "Let a line L and two coordinate systems, C and C', on L be given. There exist two numbers A and B with $A \neq 0$, such that for any point on L, its coordinate x in C is related to its coordinate x' in C' by the equation $x' = Ax + B$."

   My students decided to try to construct a general proof because they were not satisfied with the "proof by example" shown in the text.

   The essential postulate here is Postulate 13: "Let A and A' be any two distinct points and let B and B' be any two distinct points. Then, for every pair of distinct points P and Q in space,

   $$\frac{PQ \text{ (relative to } \{A, A'\})}{PQ \text{ (relative to } \{B, B'\})} \text{ is a constant."}$$

9

Guided by the example in the text we finally came up with the following argument which served as a basis for discussion.

$$\frac{|x-a|}{|x'-a'|} \overset{(1)}{=} \frac{|b-a|}{|b'-a'|} \overset{(2)}{\longrightarrow} \left(\frac{x-a}{x'-a'} = \frac{b-a}{b'-a'} \lor \frac{x-a}{x'-a'} = \frac{a-b}{b'-a'}\right) \overset{(3)}{\dashv}$$

$$\frac{|x-b|}{|x'-b'|} \overset{(1)}{=} \frac{|b-a|}{|b'-a'|} \overset{(2)}{\longrightarrow} \left(\frac{x-b}{x'-b'} = \frac{b-a}{b'-a'} \lor \frac{x-b}{x'-b'} = \frac{a-b}{b'-a'}\right) \overset{(3)}{\dashv}$$

$$\overset{(3)}{\longrightarrow} \left(\overbrace{x' = \frac{b'-a'}{b-a}x + \frac{a'b-ab'}{b-a}}^{r} \lor \overbrace{x' = -\frac{b'-a'}{b-a}x + \frac{a'b+ab'-2aa'}{b-a}}^{s} \right)$$
$$\overset{(3)}{\longrightarrow} \left(\underbrace{x' = \frac{b'-a'}{b-a}x + \frac{a'b-ab'}{b-a}}_{r} \lor \underbrace{x' = -\frac{b'-a'}{b-a}x + \frac{2bb'-a'b-ab'}{b-a}}_{t} \right) \Bigg\} \overset{(4)}{\dashv}$$

$$\overset{(4)}{\longrightarrow} \underbrace{x' = \frac{b'-a'}{b-a}x + \frac{a'b-ab'}{b-a}}_{r} \overset{(5)}{\dashv}$$

$$\overset{(5)}{\longrightarrow} x' = Ax + B \text{ where } A = \frac{b'-a'}{b-a}, B = \frac{a'b-ab'}{b-a}, \text{ and } A \neq 0.$$

To facilitate discussion of the reasons for steps (3) and (4)

Let r represent the statement $x' = \dfrac{b'-a'}{b-a}x + \dfrac{a'b-ab'}{b-a}$.

Let s represent the statement $x' = -\dfrac{b'-a'}{b-a}x + \dfrac{a'b+ab'-2aa'}{b-a}$.

Let t represent the statement $x' = -\dfrac{b'-a'}{b-a}x + \dfrac{2bb'-a'b-ab'}{b-a}$.

The statement $\sim(s \land t)$ is easily proved. Thus step (4) takes the form
$[(r \lor s) \land (r \lor t) \land \sim(s \land t)] \longrightarrow r$.

According to 12(b) and (c), this proves r provided $[(r \lor s) \land (r \lor t) \land \sim (s \land t)]$ $\longrightarrow r$ is a tautology as asserted by (vi). This assertion is readily verified by means of an 8-line truth table.

Those of use who use the axiomatic method know that it brings a new excitement to the classroom. We use it for the purpose of improving our expositions and not for any desire to be ultra-rigorous. We certainly do not assume the burden of proving every proposition we encounter. On the other hand we believe that, sooner or later, it becomes fatuous to keep talking about proof and presenting so-called proofs without telling the student what a proof is 12(c). We must give him some touchstone, some criterion, which will enable him to judge for himself whether or not a given argument is valid.

For example, he can judge that B (page 1) is valid because it is essentially a form of tautology (*iv*), and that C (page 2) is valid because its overall structure is that of tautology (*v*).

A student who can apply such criteria has acquired new dimensions of understanding. He should be encouraged to apply these criteria to his own arguments—and to ours.

We know that long lists of carefully worded postulates are often criticized and derided. The following "Protractor Postulate" from the SMSG, *Geometry with Coordinates*, "If M is any plane and if $\overrightarrow{VA}$ and $\overrightarrow{VB}$ are noncollinear rays in *M*, then there is a unique ray coordinate system in *M* relative to *V* such that $\overrightarrow{VA}$ corresponds to 0 and such that every ray $\overrightarrow{VX}$ with *X* and *B* on the same side of $\overrightarrow{VA}$ corresponds to a number less than 180," will seem pretty formidable to a teacher whose "protractor postulate" is a statement to the effect that every student must have a protractor. Nevertheless the SMSG "Protractor Postulate" is an essential link in a very significant exposition which enables the student to use his knowledge of real numbers in the study of geometry.

We know, too, that formal proofs are often denounced as a particularly pedantic and artificial way to belabor the obvious—although I have never heard this charge made by a teacher who has presented such proof in the classroom. Experienced teachers know that it is the "obvious" that often blocks student understanding. Flow-diagram proofs do not create new difficulties. They merely expose the difficulties that are already there. Is it better to ignore these difficulties or to examine them forthrightly? We know, of course, that the student will not encounter flow-diagram proofs in advanced courses in mathematics. For this reason we encourage the use of essay proofs during the last semester of the twelfth grade. However, this writer is convinced that there is no substitute for the flow-diagram format when the student is learning the structure of proof in grades nine through eleven. The construction of such a proof demands the same level of understanding that is required to program for a computer.

Those who believe that teachers should encourage the development of intuition and the construction of plausible arguments should have no quarrel with this axiomatic method. Every formal proof is preceded by many introductory exercises, experiments, and conjectures. Many plausible arguments are presented by both teacher and pupil.

Those who carry the banner for "discovery" and for "multiple attack" on problems should be particularly enthusiastic about the axiomatic method. As noted earlier the multicontrapositive concept 10 suggests as many as $n + 1$ different attacks on the proof of a theorem the hypothesis of which is a

11

conjunctive statement having n clauses. Some of these may be very easy to prove while others are difficult or even impossible. Students are intrigued by the problem of selecting the one that is easiest to prove and by the fact that one proof will suffice to establish $n + 1$ mutually equivalent statements. After a student has verbalized all of the n (partial) contrapositives of a theorem having n clauses in its hypothesis, he begins to understand what the theorem says.

Discovery is encouraged by assignments that require the student to explore the converses of a theorem that has been proved, to verbalize each, and decide whether it is true or false. I guarantee that this procedure will confront the class with a wealth of nontrivial conjectures which are not found in any text. Each conjecture poses a small research problem. If the student believes that it is true, he is required to supply a proof. He may, of course, prove the conjecture false by providing a counterexample.

Thus, if we are dealing with quadrilaterals, the theorem

$$
\begin{array}{ll}
\text{(a)} \ \overline{AB} \parallel \overline{DC} \\
\text{(b)} \ \overline{AD} \parallel \overline{BC}
\end{array} \right\} \rightarrow
\left\{
\begin{array}{ll}
\overline{AB} \cong \overline{DC} & (1) \\
\overline{AD} \cong \overline{BC} & (2) \\
\angle A \cong \angle C & (3) \\
\angle D \cong \angle B & (4)
\end{array}
\right.
$$

has 14 partial converse forms, six of which are distinct after they are verbalized. Of these six, four are true. The converse whose hypothesis is $(1) \wedge (3)$ is particularly intriguing.

The axiomatic method possesses no special properties which exempt it from the general rule that the success of any method of exposition depends upon the teacher. However, the axiomatic method gives the mathematics teacher a reasonable chance to succeed in his efforts to render himself dispensable by enabling his students to think for themselves. His mission is accomplished if he can teach young people not what to think—but *how to think*.

■ *Albert A. Blank*

THE USE AND ABUSE OF THE AXIOMATIC METHOD
IN HIGH SCHOOL TEACHING

The revisions of the mathematics curriculum in the United States have one truly modern feature, a deep-running current against the teaching of mathematics as dogma. The surface signs of this current are often confusing and easily misread. Sometimes it seems that we have merely replaced the traditional orthodoxy with a new one as rigid and hidebound as the old. Yet, the curriculum now set in motion is not soon to be quiescent again. There is a healthy stir generated by the attempt to formulate rational objectives for the curriculum and by experimentation to increase its effectiveness in meeting those objectives. The innovator is impelled to argue persuasively for the changes he seeks; the traditionalist, for the status quo, and both are pushed to obtain a genuine measure of methods by their effects. We learn by degrees that there are no pat answers to the curricular problem; we can no more avoid the work of framing and testing our hypotheses here than anywhere else. We have come to believe that mathematics should not be taught by rule of thumb and rote. We want to develop and build upon intuition, to lead the student to argue, to question, and to conjecture, to persuade him of the need for logical reason and deduction. Good teachers have always been able to accomplish these things in any curriculum, but now we are ambitiously trying to create a curriculum with texts to stimulate this kind of teaching and learning.

The introduction of new topics and new terminology, although it receives the greatest public attention, is not a significant change. The backbone of the curriculum remains the traditional syllabus. There is a real gain in the reduced emphasis or omission of conventional matter which at best has questionable value for later development. In this way we are provided with a bonus of time in which we may try to do more interesting and useful things. For example, in grades six to eight, which formerly were devoted largely to arid and ineffective arithmetic drill, there is a substantial turn toward elementary algebra, elementary number theory, and intuitive geometry. In elementary and intermediate algebra, the topic of factorization is losing its former pre-eminence. "Solution of triangles" has become a lesser concern in trigonometry in favor of the development of the analytic properties of circular functions. In analytic geometry the stress on the detailed properties of conic sections and on the treatment of conics in general position with the rotation formulas seems to be diminishing. In fact, both trigonometry and analytic geometry seem to be on the verge of disappearing as separate sub-

13

jects, their topics being distributed among geometry, intermediate algebra, and calculus. The calculus itself is starting to make its place in the space left at the head of the high school curriculum. Although there has been a great deal of pother about the "new" mathematics, the significant changes lie in the reorganization and illumination of the traditional curriculum. The new topics introduced to examplify and clarify draw a great deal of attention because of their novelty alone and so tend to be overemphasized in teaching. (Presumably, with familiarity, such topics as sets and nondecimal numeration will in time receive no more than their proper emphasis.)

When we try to teach mathematics rationally, we usually try to adopt the axiomatic method of instruction, that is, we lay out a set of postulates before the student and proceed to derive the theorems of our subject in a tidy sequence. The method has a seeming effectivenes. Certainly a great many mathematicians were first captivated by geometry in which the use of the axiomatic method is an old story. From nonmathematicians, too, we often hear that geometry is the only mathematics which ever awakened their interest. Furthermore, the mathematician, with a professional need for absolute clarity about his assumptions and complete security in the logical chain of argument by which his conclusions are justified, is inclined to take his own necessities for the needs of students at all levels. Also in training teachers and graduate students, we are inclined to emulate the smooth work of the Bourbaki hydra, but forget that the work is more an encyclopedia than a set of texts—and these, our students, go out and tend to teach in the same manner as they were instructed. All in all, the axiomatic method seems to be deeply imbedded in our thinking about curricular reform.

The pacesetting texts in the revisions of high school algebra are quite uniform in adopting a postulational approach to the number system. The material is hardly inspirational, but in the hands of the curricular leaders it has been rescued from unredeemed dullness. If a student is luckless enough to be using a derivative text, however, he is likely to be drilled in the field postulates to the point of nausea. We seem to feel that to be honest, to tell all with utmost explicitness, is a virtue sufficient unto itself. But the student must be prepared to hear. We cannot neglect the fundamental principle of pedagogy: first, get his attention. The children of friends and neighbors often come to me for help with their difficulties in algebra; their complaint is not that the material is obscure or that the exercises are terribly difficult, but that the material is so boring and tedious they cannot concentrate on it or keep it in memory. They regard it with apathy if not antipathy. The material is destroying the motivation to learn. No doubt, the children who come to me for help constitute an extremely biased sample, but there is a plain warning here that the "new" mathematics can be poisoned by the same insensitive pedagogy as was the old.

14

These remarks about the axiomatic method of teaching elementary algebra may seem to indicate only that the method may backfire in the hands of a poor teacher, but I believe that, in fact, the axiomatic method of instruction encourages unimaginative teaching, lends itself to excessive formal drill, and restricts creativity. We no longer take the attitude that axioms are self-evident truths, but we often do something far worse. We adopt the attitude that the axioms of a mathematical system (together with axioms of logic) are the ground rules for a formal game in which the desiderata are logical accuracy and consistency. Although we have removed the dogma from mathematics in this way, have we not been too timid to proclaim that this is a purposeful activity and not merely accidentally useful? It is no wonder that so many students fail to relate this game to any human concern of their own (unless it be the ulterior concern to get satisfactory grades as a passport to college and the job beyond). We do tell the students that what we teach will eventually prove significant and useful—for too many of these students the trouble is that the great by-and-by never comes. For all the brain flogging, the mathematics lies in disuse and is quickly forgotten; all that remains is a vague memory of unpleasantness.

I did remark that geometry, where the axiomatic method of teaching is traditional, has proved to be a captivating subject. It could hardly be the axiomatic method of instruction which is responsible, but could well be the fascination of the direct interplay between the world of physical (spatial) experience and the world of ideas. Sometimes we forget that Euclidean geometry is applied mathematics. For geometry there is a setting in which the student can experiment and formulate conjectures. Once he has begun to make his own conjectures, he is well motivated to test them logically against known propositions and other conjectures. In geometry, at least, we have not yet completely hidden the mode of thought which makes his subject so exciting to a research mathematician. Geometry has the advantage of being sufficiently close to common experience that long specialized training is not needed to manipulate its concepts. Furthermore, the exercises of geometry repay the student's efforts. Is there any better way of teaching the values of mathematical formalism and deduction than by application to a problem for which the solution could hardly be foreseen by a naive intelligence? Even the weakest geometry text is rich in such problems.

Contrast the problem work in a geometry text with that in a typical algebra text. In the algebra, the exercises for a given lesson are likely to contain a great deal of routine drill with long sequences of exercises which demand no more than a parroting of some methodical development of the day's lesson with nothing more than a change of lettering or other symbolic complication as a slight relief from the monotony. The exercises for a geometry lesson seldom convey such a sense of tedious repetition. Although the geometry

15

exercises may be intended to reinforce a limited range of concepts, the exercises and their solutions have distinctive individual features which lend a variety and richness to the experience of solving problems in geometry often lamentably absent in algebra. To teach algebra axiomatically can scarcely be the cure for this disease.

We should not uncritically accept the axiomatic method of teaching as a pedagogical device. The axiomatic exposition of a mathematical discipline usually represents a fairly advanced state of development, and for good reason. It is highly unlikely that a mathematician will contemplate a blank sheet of paper and completely out of his fertile imagination write down a set of axioms for an entirely new mathematical system which has any great interest for the mathematical community. Mathematics simply does not grow by such leaps. The process of axiomatization is evolutionary; it may develop from a search for interrelations and simplifications in a body of propositions, perhaps some conjectural, or it may develop by small modifications of known systems. We hide this evolutionary development from the student by beginning our teaching with so mature a point in the development of a mathematical system as an axiomatic formulation. He may well excused if he adopts the attitude that mathematics is a complete and perfect structure, something which he may study and appreciate, but scarcely something he has to do anything about. It is a wonder, if we succeed in engaging their attention at all, that some of our students do choose eventually to get into the game, rather than remain forever on the sidelines as spectators.

There is a place for the axiomatic method of teaching in areas where the student already has considerable knowledge of the subject matter and the purpose is to organize and summarize that knowledge. For example, in a first calculus for superior students, we may wish to be somewhat precise in our exposition of the concept of limit and therefore make a careful presentation of the real number system. It seems reasonable to avoid the lengthy constructive approach to the number system and to gain time by introducing the real number system axiomatically as a complete ordered field. The only likely novelty is the axiom of completeness, and this can be presented in a provocative, interesting fashion.

Although the axiomatic method does not seem to be an appropriate vehicle for teaching new ideas, we need not use the axiomatic method of teaching to teach axiomatic method. I do not mean to be playing on words, but to emphasize the distinction between teaching our codified knowledge and teaching the processes by which our knowledge is organized and codified. The former approach is hard to motivate and tends to bring out the drill-master in the best of teachers; the latter is bound to arouse curiosity and excitement, but it demands much greater intellectual commitment on the part of teacher and student. The teaching of axiomatic method involves

16

teaching what a mathematician does, not just what he concludes. There would be a preliminary exploratory phase in which theorems are obtained or conjectured on a heuristic basis. As the body of knowledge grows, the phase of codification may begin. What theorems are deduced from which? Are the hypotheses formulated as economically as they might be? Are the conditions known to be sufficient for a certain result also necessary? Have we defined our concepts carefully enough to reason about them unambiguously? By answering these questions, we begin to perceive structural relations among our theorems and begin to acquire some sense of what kind of proof is needed in the area of study. Eventually, we come to realize that the propositions of our system can be derived from those of a very limited subset and, similarly, that the concepts of our system can be defined in terms of those of an appropriate subset. These subsets of concepts and propositions may then be taken as undefined terms and provisional postulates for our system. Ultimately, we may pursue the quest for a more refined structure by such canons of mathematical good taste as simplicity and brevity. In this phase, we may lose some students—after all, the refinement of an axiomatic structure is an extremely sophisticated endeavor—but by then the important theorems and their interrelations should have been covered and the student should have acquired substantial mathematical maturity.

We can only imagine how the syllabus for a high school course would look if such an approach were adopted. Surely it does not pay, in algebra, to dig into elementary arithmetic this way just to end up with such small potatoes as the field postulates. In geometry, the number of possibilities is staggering. For example, we could begin with the concept of area on an intuitive basis and obtain most of the common elementary results by slicing up figures. (Initially, of course, we would take the existence of such simple figures as squares for granted, take the homogeneity of space as tacit, and lightly pass over the hard issues raised by incommensurable quantities.) The Pythagorean Theorem could then be obtained early by the method of subdividing a square. With this theorem, the essence of Euclidean geometry is in the palm of the hand, and there are any number of directions which could be taken including even the early introduction of analytic geometry and vector concepts. Several possible continuations come to mind, but to write out a detailed prescription at this point would work against the essential value of such an approach, its great freedom. Besides, I feel that a really satisfactory effort along these lines would require several years of collaboration between mathematicians and high school teachers, and there would have to be a lengthy schedule of experimentation and revision based on the evaluation of the material as it is tried in the classroom—hardly a pencil-and-paper operation. The important point is that such an approach is possible, it looks very exciting, and it is not being tried. No student who completes such a course could fail to appreciate Euclid's accomplishment.

17

There is no good reason to expend the effort of devising such an approach upon unsuitable material, and this naturally takes us back to the problem of how to handle ninth-grade algebra. My own feeling is that the entire subject can be distributed among the elementary grades. The exciting thing about elementary algebra is the method of writing general arithmetic propositions by appropriate symbolic techniques. These techniques are already being taught in the primary grades to some degree, and there seems to be no reason why children should not obtain a firm operational grasp of the algebraic manipulations permitted by the field postulates by the time they complete sixth or seventh grade with an accompanying enhancement of the usual elementary arithmetical skills. The most advanced topics usually taught in elementary algebra are the solution of second order linear systems and the solution of quadratic equations. These topics could certainly be covered by the end of the eighth grade together with much else, say a large amount of intuitive geometry and some elementary number theory. There is no visible reason why students should not be prepared for a substantial course in geometry at ninth-grade level, and even now there are a few thousand students each year who take geometry in grade nine. The tenth and eleventh grades should build more effectively upon the kind of mathematical maturity developed in the geometry and serve to prepare for calculus in the twelfth grade. It is incomprehensible that we have for so long treated the courses following geometry by disregarding the intellectual development which a good geometry course implies. The function concept should be introduced early in conjunction with coordinate and vector methods and the flavor of trigonometry modified accordingly. We do not want the ideas of proof to be forgotten; we should introduce mathematical induction so that proof need not be confined to trivial material. The work on elementary functions should be designed with a view toward the developments of the calculus. Thus, logarithmic and exponential functions should still be studied through their algebraic properties, that is, through the homomorphisms between the additive and the multiplicative groups on the real continuum, but continuity should be revealed as an assumption even though a satisfactory treatment must be deferred to the calculus. Inequalities should be employed systematically rather than, as in some texts, brought in topically without much general use.

I do not think much importance should be placed upon present unpreparedness of teachers to handle such a curriculum. We cannot expect teacher training to be appropriately modified unless such a curriculum exists. A great deal can be done by assisting the teacher in service. We may safely presume if a teacher has the ability, he certainly does not have the time to work up a large number of illustrative examples and counterexamples, or to find alternative proofs of theorems and alternative solutions to problems, or to research the history of his subject, its applications, and its further development. One of

18

the most effective forms of assistance is to couple texts with teachers' manuals written with an explicitness and thoroughness far beyond what we are accustomed to. One of the most important reasons for the success of new curricular programs, little noted in most public critiques, is the unusual adequacy of the teachers' manuals they provide. I am somewhat skeptical of the value of summer institutes or special undergraduate courses for prospective mathematics teachers as preparation for the teaching of such a curriculum. It seems to me that the teacher is better motivated and learns best how to handle such material by facing the daily problem of conducting a class through it.

One of the most important results of the recent curricular innovations has been the great stimulus they have provided teachers to improve their understanding of mathematics in the process of investigating alternative approaches and trying to evaluate them. No longer do teachers think of the mathematics curriculum as an immutable structure, but as something we may experiment with, improve, and adapt to fit the scientific and mathematical temper of the times. They carry this experimental inquiring attitude into the classroom and provoke the kind of intellectual commitment we want to see in our students. Teachers now talk excitedly about Socratic method, about motivation, about discovery. We cannot hope to maintain this healthy ferment by continual large-scale revision of the curriculum; we should try to build it into the curriculum directly by writing each course so that the process of inquiry is not easily supplanted by rote learning. We should teach axiomatic method, not use the axiomatic method of teaching.

■ *R. C. Buck*

THE ROLE OF A NAIVE AXIOMATICS

Education is a process of learning to draw finer and finer distinctions between similar things, and of organizing these into more and more elaborate structures. The naive two-valued world of our youth becomes the gray world of our maturity, and the simple things become complex. In mathematics, too, the firm sureties of the freshman become the philosophical doubts of the graduate.

In its report of 1959, the Commission on Mathematics of the CEEB laid stress upon *structure* and *axiomatics*. In this, it was calling attention to serious defects in the traditional mathematics curriculum, particularly in the area of algebra. Here, for too long, there was rote learning of special skills with little if any treatment of the underlying logical pattern. The Commission called for more attention to the deductive structure of algebra and for a greater reliance upon general principles rather than upon special tricks.

These points deserved to be made, and made loudly. However, in the hands of some who perhaps do not understand the role of axiomatics in mathematics, these points have been exaggerated and carried to extremes that are certainly unwise, and probably harmful. Unfortunately, we as mathematicians are at fault in that we have not communicated our attitudes toward our subject to the general community. Too often, we have allowed others to speak in our behalf, and in so doing, have allowed a distorted picture of the nature of modern mathematics to be widespread. A concern for axiomatics represents only a small portion of the activity of a professional mathematician, and even less for the professional scientists for whom mathematics is a tool. These concepts may be useful parts of the framework upon which one hangs the body of mathematics, but it is wrong to convey the impression that they constitute the central core of the subject itself.

The term axiomatics is used to describe a number of different aspects of mathematics, and the axiomatic approach touches the mathematician's life at many different points. On what I shall call the naive level, it plays a very important *descriptive* role. We are interested in a specific piece of reality, and we want to discover its properties. Our first step is to prepare a list of those properties which we already know or believe to be true. We then endeavor to extend this list by adjoining all the logical implications of these.

At the same time, this is often accompanied by a rather subtle problem. The "reality" the properties of which we seek usually does not belong to the

20

world of concrete experience; it may be an abstraction from it, a Platonic ideal which resides in the conceptual world of the mind. In this case, we are apt to say that the list of basic properties we selected to codify our beliefs forms a set of *axioms*, and the deduced list of statements become *propositions*. We may then speak of the abstract system as a *model* for reality, and we are often willing to use the deduced propositions as a guide in making decisions and predictions about the concrete reality from which the Platonic abstraction was obtained.

Geometry is the classic illustration of this process. We accept as a starting point a list of properties of entities we call points, lines, and planes, and our main purpose is to use these to deduce other interesting and less apparent properties of the space we live in. Of course, these are not properties of the concrete world of pencil marks on paper, but rather of a conceptual space that is visible in our imagination. Nevertheless, it does not surprise us to find that the pencil medians of a pencil triangle do in fact seem to be concurrent. (Indeed, would we not be dismayed if this did not happen?)

Nor is geometry the only instance of this. The concept of *modelling* is a fundamental one in mathematics. It is at the heart of all applications of mathematics and is at the central core of some of the most abstract pure mathematics. A similar approach is sometimes used in physics: "We are going to study a subject called mechanics, and here is a basic list of laws I wish to assume. I believe these laws because of the following experiments which have been carried out. Now, we will see what deductions can be made from these laws, and we will test them as predictions of the behavior of reality. If they fail, it is because of experimental error, or because we have found an instance in which the model does not resemble reality, and therefore know that in some way, our basic assumptions do not reflect a true picture of reality."

The traditional naive axiomatic approach to geometry is therefore in agreement with sound mathematical practice. It is up to the curriculum designer to be sure that an acceptable deduction scheme is followed and that no obvious blunders are committed in the choice of an axiom list, such as omitting crucial statements. Repetition is no vice; it is much better to formulate things so that students can move quickly to the point of proving results that are interesting and even surprising. One of the weaknesses of some of the so-called modern approaches to geometry is that too much stress is laid on the deduction of one intuitively apparent result from others that are only a little more intuitively apparent. There is no need whatsoever to attempt to deal with a minimal list of axioms for geometry, on the first exposure. The course in geometry should be a study of *geometry*, not abstract axiomatics for its own sake. Go as quickly as possible to the theorems on concurrence.

Prove that the process for constructing a pentagon works. And perhaps even prove Morley's theorem on the trisectors of the angles of a triangle! (While this holds no prospect of any future usefulness, it still remains a truly remarkable discovery, one well worthy of a student's attention.)

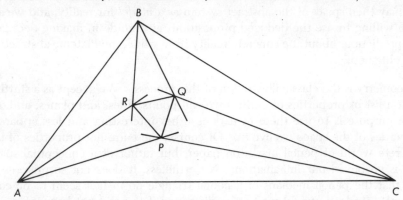

MORLEY'S THEOREM. The trisectors of ABC determine an equilateral triangle PQR

A similar viewpoint should be presented when a student first encounters the axiomatics of the number system. The student has had ample experience with measurement, and with simple calculations. He has had some informal experience with negative numbers, both integers and rationals. (In these days of -5 hours, $-30°$F., and -6 yards rushing, this requirement seems entirely reasonable; many other ways to give students a meaningful experience with negative numbers are possible, as is shown for example by the experiments of the Cambridge Conference, and many other research groups.) With this experience, the student is quite prepared to help formulate the basic axioms for a field as a codification of the properties of the elementary numerical operations.

Having formulated these axioms as observations, the student is then ready to use these to derive other properties of the system. If $\frac{a}{b}$ is the solution of the equation $bx = a$, then one may prove that

$$\frac{a}{b} + \frac{c}{d} = \frac{ad + bc}{bd}.$$

The student will then get pleasure from checking that this formula indeed works with $a = \frac{2}{3}, b = \frac{4}{11}, c = \frac{1}{6}, d = \frac{3}{5}$. (I have found college freshmen who were led to believe that this formula worked only when a, b, c and d were integers!)

There is grave danger that the statement in the Commission report about giving "more attention to the deductive structure of algebra" can be misinterpreted, with the result that this phase is spun out to a ridiculous length.

Students may even be given a tiresome sequence of "theorems" to prove by means of the commutative and associative laws, such as:

$$(x + y) + (z + w) = (x + w) + (y + z)$$

These statements are dull, and the student learns very little about the number system from them. A little of this goes a *very* long way, and even a good student is to be forgiven if his interest flags. The purpose of the axiomatics is to help a student understand the nature of the number system better, not to emphasize axiomatics as an end in themselves. Teachers and textbook writers must remember that only a tiny handful of their students will become practicing professional mathematicians, and not all of these will be greatly concerned with the minutia of axiomatics.

If something algebraic, with the same richness of theorems as geometry, is desired as an area for students to explore, and thereby gain experience in discovering and presenting proofs, why not consider elementary number theory? One may start with a set of axioms describing the integers and cover almost all of some elementary texts on the subject with students in high school or perhaps even in junior high. This would be far superior to some of the dull and tasteless presentations of "the deductive structure of the number system" which are presently being given the same students.

There are two other aspects of this part of algebra that must not be forgotten. The first is that, on the elementary level, there is a profound difference between the axiom list for Euclidean geometry and the axiom list for a field (or even an ordered field). With the former, one is very close—in a deductive sense—to a rich collection of accessible interesting theorems. With the latter, one is quite far from such a collection, and even the simplest of these must wait upon the development of the ring of polynomials over a field. It is therefore far better to spend only the briefest time on deriving secondary results about fields from the field axioms and proceed as quickly as possible to the treatment of polynomials. This is not to throw deduction out the window, for there will be ample opportunity for careful reasoning as the student ascends into the more structured and sophisticated levels of algebra.

The second important difference between geometry and algebra, on this most elementary level, is that one encounters in the axiomatization of the number system in a simple form, one of the most striking achievements of mathematics. This is the realization that one can study whole collections of mathematical systems at one and the same time. One says: "I have a specific system in mind that interests me; I will list a set of axioms that describe certain basic properties of this system, and then I will explore the properties shared by the category of *all* systems that obey these axioms." This step which we customarily take without thinking was not always so easy. It is worth remembering that the founders of group theory seemed always to think in terms of spe-

23

cific permutation groups and that the general concept of abstract group was slow in coming.

For example, suppose that we have formulated the field axioms in response to the need to codify the laws for rational numbers. Turning to the real numbers (viewed as unending decimals and associated with the points on a line), it is then possible to make convincing the fact that they too obey these same axioms. At the same time, a finite field such as Z_7 can be examined, and perhaps one may also introduce the complex field. All of these make evident the fact that the field axioms do not describe a unique structure; they are not *categorical*, or *vollständig*. By choosing to single out this special list of properties of the rational numbers, one has arrived at a very useful general structure or category which has many specific realizations. This phenomenon is easy to illustrate in algebra; while it can be done in geometry, it is much harder, for the examples are apt to seem contrived and artificial.

There are some curriculum designers who have taken a totally different approach. Taking as their start any of the current reworkings of Landau's *Grundlagen*, they seem to have misunderstood its basic purpose and meaning. They have read from these, as a dogmatic statement: "a rational number is a class of equivalent ordered pairs of integers" and "a negative integer is an equivalence class of ordered pairs of whole numbers," and have therefore argued that if this is what a negative integer, or a rational number *is*, then we ought to tell this to children as soon as possible so they will not be confused about this important subject.

The key to the understanding of both the synthetic approach to number, exemplified so well by Landau, and its raison d'être is the pair of words model and consistency, without which any discussion of axiomatics would be incomplete. They are of great importance for anyone who has achieved the requisite level of mathematical and philosophical sophistication: they have little significance for the more elementary levels of mathematical attainment and interest.

Suppose that, by some motivation, we have been led to prepare a list of axioms for some specific system or category of systems. How do we know that this list does not allow contradictory implications? (Example: a Very Naive Set Theory which allows the free construction of sets also allows Russell's paradox, and also Burali-Forti's.) For instance, how can we be sure that there are not hidden inconsistencies even in the axioms for a field? The solution of this problem again involves the use of models, this time models of one mathematical system within another system.

The standard technique is to exhibit an example of the system, on the grounds that what *exists* must be free of contradiction. We would show that the field axioms are consistent by producing the field Z_2, or Z_7. But, suppose the axiom list included the order axioms for the real field and therefore, are not satisfied by a finite field; is it sufficient to point to our intuitive understanding of the Platonic line and its conceptual existence in order to guarantee the internal consistency of these axioms? Clearly not! We must therefore construct a model for the real line within some other established reality in such a way that all the given axioms are satisfied by this model. But, does this indeed settle the matter of consistency or does it merely transfer the question to the *other* reality? For this reason, all that can be done in many cases is to demonstrate that axiom lists have relative consistency.

The purpose of the lengthy synthesis of the number system presented in Landau is to show that the axioms are consistent, relative to the assumed consistency of a suitable axiomatic set theory. A model is therefore to be built within set theory for the integers, the rationals, and the reals. But, *a model is not the thing itself*, and one should not therefore say that a rational number *is* a certain class of ordered pairs of classes of ordered pairs of collections of sets. (And think how much worse this becomes if one insists that each ordered pair be modelled in the form $<a, b> = \{\{a\}, \{a, b\}\}$.)

Those curriculum designers who have attempted to follow this Landau pattern in developing the number system in elementary and junior high school may have felt that such a formalized treatment gave more meaning and concrete substance to the nonrigorous and intuitive concept of negative number and "fractions" which children brought to the classroom. On the contrary, I believe that children have a strong intuitive feeling for the number line, and are quite willing to use it as a basis for a model of the number system. It is hypocrisy to give them an elaborate model, nested like Chinese boxes, which rests ultimately upon their shadowy version of abstract set theory. Let them be given instead analogies with things they have seen, touched, and experienced like yardsticks, temperature, and time. If they *must* see a demonstration of relative consistency, let it be that of Euclidean geometry, done analytically in terms of the number system.

Of course, every serious mathematics student should meet the detailed synthesis of the number system at some stage in his career. It is best made an independent student project, for as anyone who has tried it knows, this is extremely dull stuff to do completely in class. Moreover, it has its greatest value if the experience is deferred until the student has at hand other mathematical systems to which a similar construction can be profitably applied. For example, when he has seen and worked with a number of integral domains, he can be shown in half an hour that a process exists for embedding any integral domain in a field. This should be illustrated at once by observing that one may use this to construct the rational field from the domain of integers and to construct the field of rational forms from the ring of polynomials; if the background is adequate, one may also point to the Mikusinski development of distributions. Similarly, the use of Cauchy sequences to go from the

25

rational numbers to the reals is given its proper role in the context of completing a metric space.

The proper time for these topics is college, and I see no useful purpose to be achieved in moving isolated fragments of this down into elementary school. Indeed, where the students are not mature enough to understand the philosophical viewpoint behind the approach, I have real fears that harm can result instead. It could produce a lost generation, ill at ease with arithmetic because they cannot look at "¾" without being reminded of the Chinese boxes, and the resulting complexity that masquerades behind this simple facade.

In summary then, I strongly favor a developmental treatment of axiomatics in which three main levels of sophistication are encountered:

(1) *The naive or descriptive level.* Here, axioms are formulated to describe or codify basic properties of an existing system and are then used to derive additional properties of the system.

(2) *The structural level.* Here, the point of view shifts from the study of a single individual system to the study of a category of systems, all of which share the same axiom set. At this stage, we study Abelian groups, or commutative rings, and our interest is in seeing how these various groups or rings relate to each other and how, for example, some can be built up from others.

(3) *The philosophical level.* Here, we shift again to an introspective study of the axiom sets themselves, and we look at such matters as consistency, redundancy, equivalence, etc. It is at this stage that we become sensitive to the axiomatic nature of logic itself, and encounter the very subtle problem of how one can make a logical analysis of the nature of logic.

Each level is important in the training of a mathematician—although it must again be emphasized that axiomatics is only a small part of what a mathematician does. Of these, only the first is important in the mathematics education of a typical layman. In pre-college courses, one should principally meet the naive level, with perhaps a touch of the structural level, and certainly none of the philosophical level. In college courses, one might meet much of level one and two, and some rare intrusions of the third level. Of course, exceptional individuals have been able to enjoy, and even make original contributions on each level, at much earlier times.

In discussing educational questions, it is obviously wise for mathematicians to remain constantly aware that they themselves represent a very small percentage of the school population. Their advice to curriculum experts and textbook writers must take this into account and lead them to take a balanced and informed position in giving recommendations for content in pre-college courses, and not overemphasize the abstract and the elegant at the expense of the motivated and the concrete.

■ *Irving Allen Dodes*

MATHEMATICS: ITS STRUCTURE, LOGIC AND METHOD

The purpose of this paper is to explore the basic elements of *academic* (as distinguished from *general*) mathematics, particularly on the secondary level, grades seven through twelve.   It is the premise of this paper that all academic mathematics rests firmly upon three basic elements: *structure, logic* and *method*. Some might say that one of these elements is more important than another.   However, an argument about relative importance would be pointless, since all three elements are absolutely essential in any course which can be dignified by the title of "mathematics."

There is, of course, a valid question associated with these basic elements: how much of each element is pedagogically sound at a specific level of a student's development?   This has no obvious general answer.   Nevertheless, certain broad principles can probably be accepted without controversy. For example, it is clear that a complicated method for solving a problem cannot be assimilated by a mathematically immature student.   This is so, not because the student cannot understand each step of the procedure, but rather because his preoccupation with the individual steps tends to inhibit a comprehension of the total performance.   This thought applies, perhaps not equally clearly, to all three elements: structure, logic and method.

Before launching into a systematic discussion of the basic elements of mathematics, it might be well to mention one other matter which tends to shape individual courses in (academic) mathematics.   Like many other subjects, mathematics has at least three aspects: a liberal-arts aspect, a propaedeutic aspect, and a service aspect.   The *liberal-arts aspect* stems from the fact that a civilized human being of today must know at least as much about mathematics and the sciences as he does about the other "humanities": the social sciences, literature, and the arts.   He need not be an expert mathematician, just as he need not be an expert historian, writer, musician or artist, but he should be able to communicate in mathematics (and the sciences) at no lower level than he does in the other areas mentioned.   The *propaedeutic aspect* stems from the fact that mathematics is a continuing experience, and that one "branch" of mathematics leads to another.   For example, many branches of higher mathematics are illuminated by linear algebra.   The *service aspect* refers to the fact that mathematics is the language of the social sciences, the natural sciences, engineering and even of some of the arts.   The "shape" of a course is inextricably bound up with the purpose and motivation of the students.   Calculus taught to a class of engineers usually differs from that taught to a class of budding mathematicians, and this is quite proper.

27

With these remarks, intended to provide a frame of reference, the remainder of this paper deals with the axiomatic method in teaching mathematics *via* the three elements of mathematics. It should be understood that the separation of the discussion into three parts is merely for convenience. In fact, the three elements are inextricably bound to each other.

1. STRUCTURE

1.1 The Nature of Structure

In the simplest of terms, structure refers to the fact that each "branch" of mathematics is based upon:

1. Undefined terms, chosen by the mathematician
2. Definitions, chosen by the mathematician
3. Postulates, chosen by the mathematician
4. Theorems
5. An underlying system of logic, chosen by the mathematician

It should be pointed out that *theorems* (propositions with truth value T) are not chosen by the mathematician and are *not* in any sense under his control. Once the other four items have been agreed upon, every proposition in the postulational system is either T or F, regardless of the mathematician. In actual practice, certain provable propositions are singled out for demonstration and emphasis, and certain methods of proof are displayed. Nevertheless, whether or not a provable proposition is displayed, emphasized or proved in a publication, it is still a theorem.

It is a basic premise of this paper that students must be aware of the structure of any branch of mathematics which they study. Otherwise, they are not learning mathematics; they are being exposed to a set of statements which are a part of knowledge, but not, in any sense, mathematics.

An immediate conclusion of this premise is that a student should always know, for each branch of mathematics, the nature of each statement used by him. For example, the reader might wish to guess at the status of the following:

1. If equals are added to equals, the results are equal.
2. Radii of a circle are equal.
3. $-1 \times -1 = +1$

In the usual development, the *first* of these should be called a theorem, the *second* is a conventionalized part of a definition, and the *third* is part of the definition of multiplication in a field and is, therefore, a postulate. These will be explained in the sequel.

An immediate concomitant of the kind of training in which knowledge of structure is "built in" is that the student is always aware of the possibility of other, new systems of mathematics in which a definition is changed, new definitions are made, or different postulates are chosen. The opposite of this approach is the common one, in textbooks, of labelling statements as: Principle, Important Fact, "Remember," Law, or by merely writing the statement with a box drawn around it. These methods are anti-mathematical in nature since they conceal the structure; they support a pretense that a sequence which was chosen for convenience or by historical accident is inexorably true and fixed; and they stifle research and speculation. It is *most* important that students know which propositions are postulates (not provable in the specific system) and which are theorems (not deniable in the specific system). Furthermore, students should be encouraged to seek the consequences of denying the postulates. This is, indeed, the important outcome of the so-called axiomatic method.

1.2 Structure in the Algebras

In a secondary school study of algebra, it would be idle to define *natural numbers* as the intersection of all σ-sets, at least at the present time. Therefore, natural numbers and, in fact, all real numbers are left undefined in this sequence. This is a perfectly satisfactory and tenable state of affairs, provided that the students are apprised of this fact. In other words, *numbers* and other undefined terms should be labeled as such.

The situation with respect to *definitions* is more complicated in that there is some disagreement about the "proper" form for a definition. In a general way, mathematicians feel that, at least in the algebras,

". . . *a definition* is simply an agreement as to how a symbol is to be used. It is a sentence that gives to a symbol, previously without meaning, the same meaning as a term already part of the theory. When the definition is given in the form "defined term = defining term," it is called a *formal definition*. When it is given in some other way, it is called *informal*. . . . Formal or informal definitions are both used in mathematics, depending upon which is convenient in a given context."[1]

On the whole, "informal" definitions using *if* or *iff* (if and only if) are probably the most common ones in mathematical works. Some examples, culled from the works of prominent mathematicians are:

"We spoke above of 'well-chosen definitions.' As an example, we introduce the notion of subgroup. . . ., If S is a subset of G and if S and G are groups with respect to the same operation, then S is called a *subgroup* of G."[2]

"We now give a definition of 'formula' . . . (1) if s and t are terms, then $(s) = (t)$ is a formula. . . ."[3]

"DEFINITION: Let N be a number system. A number z of N will be called the *one* element of the number system N if for every number a of N,

$$z \cdot a = a \cdot z = a."[4]$$

[1] Kenneth O. May, *Elements of Modern Mathematics,* Addison-Wesley Publishing Company, Reading, Mass., 1959, p. 48.

[2] May, *op. cit.,* p. 569.

[3] S. E. Kleene, *Introduction to Metamathematics,* D. Van Nostrand Company, Princeton, N. J., 1952, p. 72.

[4] Howard Levi, *Elements of Algebra,* Chelsea Publishing Company, New York, 1954, p. 59.

Similar examples can easily be found in Church, *Introduction to Mathematical Logic*; Exner and Rosskopf, *Logic in Elementary Mathematics*; MacDuffee, *An Introduction to Abstract Algebra*; Paul Rosenbloom, *The Elements of Mathematical Logic*; Rosser, *Logic for Mathematicians*; and other books on mathematics. In almost every one of these cases, the *if* could be replaced either by *iff* or by $\equiv$ to conform to the more careful usage.

The point of the preceding discussion is that definitions are usually expressed in the "reversible" *iff* form, or else an "if" which really means "iff", and that these definitions have two halves, so to speak, which are of equal status: the *if* part and the *only if* part. When algebra is taught, whether in the secondary school or any other kind of school, *both* "halves" should be emphasized. Above all, the student should be told that a statement is a definition, if it is—not that it is a "law," "principle," or a box. Before continuing with thoughts about the "parts" of a definition, it is important to note that definitions of *relations* and of *branches of mathematics* or *mathematical systems* usually or always consist of sets of statements called *postulates*. For example, the *equivalence* relation is defined by three postulates:

(1) Reflexive Postulate, e.g., $a = a$

(2) Symmetric Postulate, e.g., $(a = b) \longrightarrow (b = a)$

(3) Transitive Postulate, e.g., $(a = b) \wedge (b = c) \longrightarrow (a = c)$

Calling the three statements *R*, *S* and *T*, the definition might be written: A relation is an equivalence relation iff $R \wedge S \wedge T$. A field is, similarly, defined by eleven postulates.

It has become quite popular to discuss groups, rings and fields in secondary treatments of mathematics. This is unquestionably a tremendous step forward and it should be encouraged as much as possible. However, a certain amount of caution should be exercised in the presentation. Specifically, it is quite important from the standpoint of the future of mathematics that it be understood that the definitions of *addition* and *multiplication* must *precede* the demonstration that a set is a field. In the usual "modern" sequence for the signed numbers which leads into the discussion of the field of rational numbers, it is often "proved" that:

$$-1 \times -1 = {}^+1$$

As a matter of fact, this kind of "proof" has been used, quite frequently, to demonstrate the power of modern mathematics. This is not a good sequence. In actual fact, the number systems did not emerge from definitions of fields at all. They grew out of necessity and convenience. Part of this convenience was a set of definitions, among them the familar definitions of addition and multiplication. With the numbers as either defined or undefined terms, addition and multiplication defined in the usual arithmetic fashion, it can be *proved* that the set of rational numbers (or reals, or complex numbers) form a field *under those operations*. Strangely enough, the same people who

30

develop the idea of a field "backwards" for rational numbers or reals usually develop it correctly for the complex numbers where it is apparent that the definitions of addition and multiplication were chosen for convenience.

This is by no means a small point. In order for mathematics to develop, students must be taught that definitions and postulates are *chosen* and what the consequences of a denial of the postulates or a change of definition would be.

To be specific, a better sequence for the teaching of fields would be as follows:

(1) Teach the properties of a field *via* modulo systems.
(2) Investigate the sequence: natural numbers, integers, signed integers, rational numbers.
(3) Determine suitable definitions for addition and multiplication to make the rational numbers a field under these operations as defined.

Of course, this is an example of the axiomatic approach. It is better, from a psychological standpoint, too, than a bald unmotivated statement that the real numbers form a field and that, therefore, $^-1 \times {}^-1 = {}^+1$.

1.3 Structure in the Geometries

People think of geometry as a well-structured course. In fact, the traditional course has neither structure, logic nor (suitable) method. The very fact that few students know the status of statements like

(1) Radii of a circle are equal ("half" of a definition),
(2) Any line segment has one and only one midpoint (usually part of the Birkoff Point-Number Axiom, therefore a postulate), and
(3) If equals are added to equals, the results are equal (theorem)

is evidence that the traditional course has no structure.

A course in geometry should start with an explanation of the nature of postulational system. The undefined figures (usually, *space, surface, line* and *point*) should be discussed. All other figures, such as *angles,* should be defined in terms of the undefined figures. The definitions are usually most usable in reversible form (usually, *iff*) or as a pair of "halves" where one represents the *if* part and the other the *only if* part.

As a case in point, consider the first statement mentioned above, that about *radii of a circle.* First, define a *radius* as one line segment in the set of all possible line segments from a given point to a given curve or surface in space. Then, a *circle* is set of all points in a plane such that there exists a point in the plane (the *center*) from which the radii are equal. This is a cumbersome statement which can be "split" into two abbreviated halves, so to speak, as follows:

(1) If the radii are equal, then the figure is a circle.
(2) If the figure is a circle, then the radii are equal.

The *second* of these is further shortened to the conventional statement that

"Radii of a circle are equal." This more careful treatment leads to two other important propositions, at no extra cost:

(3) If no set of equal radii exists, then the figure is not a circle.

(4) If the figure is not a circle, then no set of equal radii exists.

It is this axiomatic attack which leads to a thorough understanding of mathematics through structure.

The treatment of *postulates*, in geometry, is even worse than the treatment of definitions. Over the years, there has been an unfortunate tendency to "postulate" any proposition which it was inconvenient to prove. Among such "postulates" were:

(1) A chord parallel to one side of a triangle divides the other sides proportionally.

(2) If equals are added to equals, the results are equal.

Some teachers like to call the first of these a postulate because it cannot be proved without the use of limits, and a proper discussion of limits is beyond the scope of the tenth-year course. However, this is not the point at all. Whether or not a proposition can be proved by elementary methods, whether or not it is convenient to prove a proposition, and whether or not there is time to prove a proposition do not enter into the designation of the "status" of the proposition. The only question is: can this proposition be denied in this postulational system? If it can, then it can be a postulate. If it cannot, it must be a theorem. The first of these is, therefore, a theorem. The same remarks are appropriate for "The area of a circle $= \pi r^2$," whether it is proved or not.

The second proposition is more interesting. Although the proof is well-known, it will bear repetition in order to make a point. Consider x, y and z ϵ S where S is a set closed under the (defined) operation of addition. Then $(x + y)$ exists in the set. Furthermore,

$$x + y = x + y$$

by the Reflexive Postulate for an equivalence relation. Now, suppose that $y = z$; in other words, y and z are names of the same mathematical object. Then $x + y = x + z$, which completes the proof of the theorem. As is easily seen, it rests upon the *definition* of equality and the *postulate* of closure, and upon nothing else. To make this proposition a postulate, one would either have to change the definition of equality or deny the postulate of closure, or both. In such a (new) system, it would have to be false or meaningless to state that "$x + y = x + y$."

1.4 Structure in the First Course in Calculus

Like any other branch of mathematics, calculus possesses a clear structure which, unfortunately, is sometimes not very clear in the first treatment. As in the algebras and geometries, the approach appears to be influenced heavily by the historical sequence of discovery. Not only does this waste precious time, but it also tends to obscure the definitions and postulates upon which the calculus rests.

Only one example will be given. In many, if not most, courses in the calculus, a strong point is often made that dy/dx is the limit of the Newton quotient and that it is *not* to be regarded as an actual quotient. Not too long after that, an equally strong point is made that dy and dx are differentials and that dy/dx is an actual quotient. (In advanced courses, the definition of a derivative is made to depend upon the gradient.) The point is that it is perfectly proper to use temporary definitions which are, at a later time, generalized to be more useful; it is all wrong to give conflicting concepts, as in this approach. Much the same comment might be made about the definitions of integrals.

2. LOGIC

2.1 The Nature of Proof

The end-product of the work of a mathematician is the production and display of a set of theorems, established by a "proof" of one kind or another. However, the idea of "proof" is a surprisingly flexible one. The purpose of a proof is to display an organized, systematic, sequential set of statements which lead from definitions, postulates and previous theorems to the conclusion in such a way that, if the definitions and postulates are accepted, then it is evident that the conclusion has given truth value T. The reader is convinced by the proof that the results are valid.

However, different readers require different amounts of convincing. The same reader, at different times in his development, requires different amounts of convincing. The concept of "a good proof" is, therefore, subjective. What is put into a proof, or left out, is a matter of the author's taste and temperament and his assessment of the level of knowledge of the reader.

2.2 Methods and Conventional Practices in Proofs

All proofs are based upon logical developments, but the *medium* of proof, so to speak, and the *emphasis* differ, depending upon the subject area and the background of the author of the proof. The following is an incomplete listing of various media:
    (1) by arithmetic
    (2) by algebra (often called a "derivation")
    (3) by truth table
    (4) by informal "direct proof"
    (5) by informal "indirect proof"
    (6) by use of symbolic logic, e.g., contrapositives
    (7) by formal "direct proof"
    (8) by formal "indirect proof"
    (9) by mathematical induction

The least important of these are probably (7) and (8); these are the most common ones in elementary treatments because they actually display the sequence of steps and reasons. One rarely finds a formal proof in a treatment above the secondary level. The most important of these are probably (5), (6) and (9); these are rarely found in treatment on the secondary level but are invariably found in higher treatments. It is undeniable that the introduction of proof by the "formal direct" method is pedagogically sound, but it should certainly be accompanied within the course by at least (5) and (6). It has been mentioned that the *emphasis* may be different. To illustrate this, the following two proofs of the Base-Angles Theorem, from two different textbooks, are offered. The first one was written for teachers:[5]

Hypothesis: $\triangle ABC$ is isosceles with $AC = BC$
Conclusion: $\angle CAB = \angle CBA$

Proof

Statement	Analysis
1. $\triangle ABC$ with $AC = BC$.	1. Hypothesis.
2. There is a point between A and B, call it "M", such that $AM = BM$.	2. Instance of an axiom.
3. There exists a unique line through C and M.	3. Instance of an axiom.
4. $CM = CM$.	4. Identity.
5. In triangles AMC and BMC, if $AC = BC$, $CM = CM$, and $AM = BM$, then $\triangle AMC \cong \triangle BMC$	5. Instance of an axiom.
6. $\therefore \triangle AMC \cong \triangle BMC$	6. Mod pon [1, 2, 4, 5]
7. Two triangles are congruent, namely AMC and BMC, if and only if their corresponding parts are equal.	7. Instance of a definition.
8. $\therefore \angle CAB = \angle CBA$	8. Mod pon [7, 6]

In the comment attached to this proof, the authors prove that AMC and BMC are triangles, and discuss "Identity."

The second proof is as follows, and has a different emphasis:[6]

Given: In $\triangle ABC$, $AB = AC$. Prove: $\angle 1 = \angle 2$
Plan: Draw the bisector of the vertex angle. Then prove that the triangles formed are congruent.

[5] Robert M. Exner and Myron S. Rosskopf, *Logic in Elementary Mathematics*, New York, McGraw-Hill Book Company, 1959, p. 98.
[6] I. A. Dodes, *Geometry*, New York, Harcourt-Brace and World, 1965, p. 110.

Steps		Reasons
*(1) $AB = AC$	G	(1) Given
*(2) Bisect $\angle BAC$ ($\angle 3 = \angle 3'$)	P	(2) Any angle can be bisected.
(3) AT divides $\triangle ABC$ into two triangles.	T	(3) Any angle bisector of a triangle divides it into two triangles.
*(4) $AT = AT$	P	(4) Reflexive Postulate
(5) $\triangle ABT \cong \triangle ACT$	P	(5) 2 $\triangle$s are $\cong$ if sas = sas.
(6) $\angle 1 = \angle 2$	HD	(6) Corresponding parts of congruent figures are equal.

In the second proof, the asterisks (*) are used to show the side-angle-side used. The middle column of letters gives the "status" of the "Reason", e.g., G = Given, P = Postulate, T = Theorem, and HD = "half-definition," i.e., the *if* or *only if* part of a definition.

It should be clear, from this example, that a "proof" can be written to emphasize the definitions, postulates and theorems of *logic*, or can be written to emphasize the definitions, postulates and theorems of the particular *branch of mathematics*, using the logic as binder. Because "proof" is subjective, either of these two, or a combination, may be most palatable to a reader. Whichever is chosen by the teacher, a strong effort should be made to convince the student that the result is a *theorem*.

Students often ask whether a *corollary* is a theorem and whether a result of a proof in a problem is a theorem. This is clear evidence of the student's lack of understanding about the structure of mathematics. There is absolutely no question about the first question: a corollary is always a theorem. It is to be regretted that the word *corollary* was invented, since it appears to set up another class of propositions which are more than postulates and less than theorems. However, no harm is done if the terminology: Theorem (Corollary) or even Corollary (Theorem) is employed. The second question is more difficult to answer because the answer depends upon the specific problem. If the problem refers to a general class of objects and if the hypothesis and conclusion are well-formed (no extraneous material), then the result certainly is a theorem. However, the usual textbook problem refers to a specific case and the hypothesis is often redundant, so that it usually is *not* a theorem.

2.3 Proof in the Algebras

On the whole, the best place to start proving is in the first course in algebra. The course should start with the elements of sets and symbolic logic. One of the first proofs is the following:[7]

$$\{x \in G \mid x + a = b\} = \{b - a\}$$

[7] I. A. Dodes and S. L. Greitzer, *Algebra I: Its Structure, Logic and Methods,* New York, Hayden Book Company, 1966.

Steps		Reasons
(1) $x + a = b$, where $a, b \in G$	G	(1) Given
(2) $(x + a) + {}^-a = b + {}^-a$	T	(2) Addition Theorem
(3) $x + (a + {}^-a) = b + {}^-a$	P	(3) Associative Postulate for a group
(4) $(a + {}^-a) = 0$	P	(4) Inverse Postulate for a group
(5) $x + 0 = b + {}^-a$	P	(5) Substitution in an equation
(6) $x + 0 = x$	P	(6) Identity Postulate for a group
(7) $x = b + {}^-a$	P	(7) Same as (5)
(8) $b + {}^-a = b - a$	D	(8) Definition of $b + {}^-a$
(9) $x = b - a$	P	(9) Same as (5)

In actual practice, some students insert more steps and some insert fewer; this is a matter of taste. (The more perceptive tend to use in-between steps to show that ${}^-a$ *exists* in the group, too.) However, this is not so important. The important fact is that in this proof there is a chance for a class to find out what is needed to convince a mathematician. This is almost the only criterion for a proof.

As students progress through a course which emphasizes the postulational system, they learn, very thoroughly, the structure of algebra and the forms of proof. Most important, perhaps, they are given the kind of background which enables them to understand, later, abbreviated proofs in mathematics and which motivates them to investigate the result of changing the definitions and postulates.

2.4 Proof in the Geometries

It is most unfortunate that geometry has usually been the first branch of mathematics in which proofs were explicit. For this purely historical reason, most proofs in traditional geometry have always been *formal direct* or *formal indirect*. Lately, in many traditional books, the latter of these types of proof has been omitted because the writing of these proofs was so cumbersome and the logic so involved. However, a hard look at geometry shows that the two most important types of proof in the geometries are undoubtedly:

(1) the informal indirect proof, and

(2) the use of contrapositive inference.

Only one example (of the second) will be given to illustrate the point.

An early, extremely important theorem of Euclidean geometry states that *any exterior angle of a triangle is greater than either remote interior angle.* A theorem (corollary) which follows immediately from this is that *for two lines in a plane, if the lines meet, then the alternate interior angles of any*

36

transversal are unequal. (If the two lines are *AC* and *BC*, the transversal is *AB*, then *ABC* forms a triangle with one of the alternate interior angles an exterior angle and the other a remote interior angle.) The contrapositive of this is *for two lines in a plane, if the alternate interior angles of any transversal are equal, then the lines are parallel.* Note that a very long indirect proof is reduced to a single step!

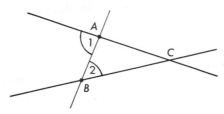

One by-product of the kind of teaching in which *different* types of proof are equally acceptable to the teacher is that students learn to test the contrapositives of each theorem. Often, the results are surprisingly good. For example, many of the theorems about unequal angles and sides in a triangle may be done in one or two steps (instead of fifteen to twenty) by using the contrapositive type of inference.

Dissatisfaction with the traditional course in geometry has led to many attempts to replace it by *vector analysis* or *analytic geometry*. There are several difficulties in these approaches, however, which make success rather unlikely. In the first place, the use of vector analysis leads to the *cosine* of an angle (if the dot product is used) and the *sine* of the angle (if the cross product is used), but not to the measure of the angle itself. The use of analytic geometry leads to the *tangent* of an angle (if slopes are used). Thus, problems leading to investigations of measures of angles must lead to ambiguous results requiring "ordinary" geometry for final clarification. A second pair of objections exists. In the case of vector analysis, the diagram is tremendously important, much more so than that in "ordinary" geometry where it may merely provide a hat-rack to hang labels. In the case of analytic geometry, the algebra is more difficult, in general, than the average tenth-year student can cope with. In either vector analysis or analytic geometry, a study of "ordinary" geometry preceding these courses greatly simplifies them. For all these reasons, it would appear more sensible to clean up the geometry course than to discard it.

2.5 Proof in the First Course in Calculus

One of the main difficulties with proofs in calculus, particularly those which involve limits, is that the authors seem to start with such strange definitions and assumptions, pulled out of a hat. For example, one proof begins: Let $\delta = m\epsilon/9$. Now, why did the author choose that value? The answer is: he knew that this would simplify the last step. At the expense of the student's equanimity, he polished the proof. Would it not have been better to say: Let $\delta = k\epsilon$, where k is a constant to be determined later? At the end of the problem, he could have used his degree of freedom to let $k = m/9$, and there would have been no mystery about the logic.

The point of this comment is that the chain of logic should be made clear, even in the calculus and even at the expense of some redundancies and inelegancies. If the reader is not convinced by the display, it is not a satisfactory proof, at least for him.

3. METHOD

3.1 The Nature of Method

A method in mathematics is a systematic approach from a problem to a "useful" form of answer. For example, a mathematical solution of $x^2 - 5x + 6 = 0$ for $x \epsilon\, C$ is

$$x = \frac{-(-5) \pm \sqrt{25 - 24}}{2} \, ,$$

but the more "useful" solutions are in $\{2, 3\}$. In fact, in one sense, the equation may be regarded as "solved" as soon as it is proved that solutions exist in the desired permissible set. (Quadratics can always be solved over the complex field and, in that sense, the written equation is a mathematical solution.)

The choice of methods depends greatly upon what kind of answer is required and what kind of knowledge the student has. To take a very simple example, consider the problem of finding $\sqrt{3}$ correct to the nearest hundredth (cnh).

Method I

```
       3. 00 00 00 )1. 7 3 2
          1
   27    |200
         |189
  343    |11 00
         |10 29
 3462       |71 00
            |69 24
             1 76
```

Method II

Guess:	1.5
Trial:	$(1.5)^2 = 2.25$
Trial:	$(1.6)^2 = 2.56$
Trial:	$(1.7)^2 = 2.89$
Trial:	$(1.8)^2 = 3.24$
Trial:	$(1.71)^2 = 2.9241$
Trial:	$(1.72)^2 = 2.9584$

Trial: $(1.73)^2 = 2.9929$
Trial: $(1.74)^2 = 3.0276$
Trial: $(1.735)^2 = 3.010225$ [too large]

Method III

Guess: 1.500

Quotient: $3.000/1.500 = 2.000$

Average $= (1.5000 + 2.000)/2 = 1.750$

Quotient $= 3.000/1.750 = 1.714$

Average $= (1.750 + 1.714)/2 = 1.732$

Quotient $= 3.000/1.732 = 1.732$

By any of the three methods (there are, of course, many more), the result is 1.73 cnh. Which should be chosen? Method I, which is the most common, is seldom understood by the student but is an excellent algorithm for obtaining the answer. Because of its efficiency, it is certainly a viable method. The one distasteful feature is that it does not fall into a postulational system as a support to the structure because it is invariably taught at a time when it would be next to impossible to demonstrate its validity.

Method II, which is one often used on desk calculators (but not on computers) is a trial-and-error method which points up the relationship between the irrational numbers and the rational numbers which are used as approximations. Besides, it is self-explanatory. However, it is tedious, and even on a desk calculator there are better methods. (Automatic square root on a desk calculator is not done this way.) Nevertheless, it is a support to the structure of mathematics.

Method III, sometimes called Newton's Method, is also very good if a desk calculator is available, but the explanation in rigorous terms[8] depends upon a knowledge of infinite series. Of course, it is self-checking so that the student is easily convinced of its validity. Nevertheless, the motivation behind this method is certainly not self-evident.

It is too bad that teachers of mathematics have to make a choice between efficient methods which cannot be explained at the time they are needed and methods which can be explained but which are tedious. One obvious recommendation is that desk calculators be purchased in profusion and that the curriculum be revised to offer explanations.

3.2 Methods in the Algebras

Almost any student can solve
$$\begin{cases} 2x + 5y = 32 \\ 3x - 4y = -7, \end{cases}$$
but it is hard to find one who can solve
$$\begin{cases} 2.1145x + 5.0023y = 31.716 \\ 3.0518x - 4.7263y = -6.9857 \end{cases}$$

[8] I. A. Dodes and S. L. Greitzer, *Numerical Analysis*, New York, Hayden Book Company, 1964, pp. 51–59.

for which $x = 4.5509$ and $y = 4.4165$. The point is not that every student should learn to do numerical problems. The point is that the curriculum, as presently constituted, is not very useful, whether it is considered from the liberal-arts aspect, the propaedeutic aspect or the service aspect. From the propaedeutic aspect, the most useful method to practice is the method of *determinants*. These are needed in *linear algebra* and in *differential equations* (to decide linear independence of solutions, for one thing). From the service aspect, the most useful method to practice is the *Gauss-Jordan Method*. The method presently taught is never useful in either sense, except in the most unusual simplified problem.

The same thought pervades the entire algebra course as presently constituted. The first course usually avoids imaginary numbers, and thus proliferates the kind of misunderstanding that leads to $\sqrt{a} \cdot \sqrt{a} = a$ (which is true only for $a \geq 0$). The same omission leads to an incomplete discussion of the solution of a quadratic and a sense of mystery about the apparent absence of X-intercepts of a parabola of the type: $y = x^2 + 1$. (The intercepts exist in the complex plane.)

A revision of the course with due respect for the various aims of the teaching of the algebras as a postulational system is more than overdue. In this revision, modern methods of the solution of problems should and must be included.

3.3 *Methods in the Geometries*

By this time, a great deal has been said about *proofs* in geometry, and many of the comments about *numerical problems* are subsumed in the preceding paragraph. However, it remains to say a few words about the general content of the geometries.

Why do some courses of study in geometry devote a precious day to a theorem about the products of segments intersecting in a circle, then not even mention powerful theorems such as Stewart's Theorem and Ceva's Theorem, both powerful tools in the solution of geometrical problems? Why do some courses of study devote a precious day to a little exercise concerning the median of a trapezoid, then not even mention the fascinating properties of cyclic quadrilaterals? In fact, what makes one topic required, one optional, and a third not even mentioned? Probably the most important factors are nonmathematical in nature: convenience, difficulty, time available, tradition, and a complex of historical allegiances. It would be more reasonable to make these important decisions on the basis of mathematical and pedagogical cogency. Does the topic or method illuminate geometry? Does it present efficient and fruitful theorems? Does it remove ambiguities? Is it useful in other branches of mathematics, and in other courses? These are some of the thoughts which should govern the judgment as to whether a topic is or is not to be required.

Tradition is so powerful in the case of geometry, a very ancient discipline,

40

that it is almost impossible to change the status of a topic without arousing an inordinate amount of emotion. A case in point is that of *constructions*. Constructions are always time-consuming, yet they serve little mathematical purpose nor are they of much practical use. Take, for example, the problem of drawing a line parallel to another line through a given point not on the given line. In the geometrical construction with straightedge and compasses, this requires two intersections with two arcs intersecting at each. Often, the lines do not even look parallel when the construction is finished. A draftsman uses a far simpler and more efficient method than a geometer. He slides one plastic triangle along another one and obtains lines that are much closer to the true parallels. Is there any interesting theory associated with constructions? Yes, of course there is. There is the problem of *constructibility*. This problem is of great interest and illuminates an important point of contact between algebra and geometry. Unfortunately, the topic of constructibility is *not* ordinarily taken up in the geometry course because the students do not have enough algebra. Then the topic of "Constructions" is taken up, at great length, with no good mathematical excuse for spending either the time or energy. (Why restrict oneself to straightedge and compasses?) It would seem that the topic of constructions might be, on any objective grounds, either omitted or made an optional curiosity, at least at this time in the student's life.

Similar remarks could be made for the entire set of topics which comprise so-called *coordinate geometry*. These have some value as a source of problems linking algebra and geometry but, on the whole, do not contribute to either from the standpoint of structure, logic or method. The time spent on constructions and coordinate geometry might be more profitably spent on symbolic logic, elementary set theory, the integration of plane and solid geometry, and an introduction to analytic geometry after *locus*.

3.4 Methods in the First Course in Calculus

To conclude, it should be noted that the same errors which are found in the usual secondary school courses are also found in the first course in calculus. Many methods are useless and are taught for purely historical reasons; other methods of great power (Simpson's Rule, Maclaurin's Series, etc.) are given skimpy treatment. The following is an actual example taken from a textbook. It deals with an integration by substitution.

Problem: Find $J = \displaystyle\int \frac{dx}{\sqrt{1 - x^2}}$

Book Solution: Let x $= \sin\theta$

Then dx $= \cos\theta\, d\theta$

And $\sqrt{1 - x^2} = \pm\cos\theta$, where the sign depends upon the value of θ

$$J = \int \frac{\cos \theta \, d\theta}{\pm \cos \theta}$$

$$J = \pm \, \theta + C$$

$$J = \pm \, \arcsin x + C$$

By a judicious choice of θ, we may write
$J = \arcsin x + C$, where the principal
value is understood.

Correct Solution: Let $x = \sin \theta$, $\theta \in \left[-\frac{\pi}{2}, \frac{\pi}{2} \right]$

Then $dx = \cos \theta \, d\theta$

And $\sqrt{1-x^2} = \cos \theta$ (There is now no ambiguity!)

$$J = \theta + C$$

$$J = \mathrm{Sin}^{-1} x + C$$

That the result is the principal value of the inverse function is neither arbitrary nor "judicious." It merely represents the interval agreed upon in the first place. If $\left[\frac{\pi}{2}, \frac{3\pi}{2} \right]$ is now chosen as the reference interval, further light is thrown on the problem. The answer will, then, not be the principal value.

4. A BLUEPRINT FOR THE FUTURE

4.1 Algebra I

It should now be possible to carry students through: an introduction to symbolic logic and the nature of proof; an introduction to sets, functions, relations and number systems leading to the concepts of groups and fields; methods for finding solution sets of equations and inequalities, including systems of these; graphs; and some right triangle trigonometry. The present anomalies leading to the lack of definition for numbers like $\sqrt{-4}$, hence to a lack of understanding of the number of roots of a quadratic with complex roots, would be avoided. Inclusion of a discussion of the complex field will clarify the entire course. If possible, enrichment topics should include simple determinants and simple problems in probability.

4.2 Geometry

It is possible, right now, to teach a course in which plane and solid geometry are not artificially separated. At the present time, such a course must be introduced by units in symbolic logic, simple set theory, the number line, and the nature of proof. It is surely evident that a good background in Algebra I will markedly reduce the number of teaching days to be spent on these concepts. This reduction will leave more time for volumes, non-Euclidean geometry, and alternate methods of proof.

4.3 Algebra II (including Trigonometry)

The greatest changes should probably take place in the *second* algebra course, including trigonometry. At the present time, this course proceeds as though there were almost no content in Algebra I. With the first course firm, the symbolic logic can be continued to quantifiers; abstract algebra can be taken through groups, rings and fields in a somewhat more rigorous fashion; set theory can be expanded to include the Boolean algebras and more advanced probability (including the Kemeny tree); the exponential, logarithmic and trigonometric functions can be discussed as isomorphisms over the reals; there is ample time for an introduction to vector and matrix spaces; and a considerable time can be spent on a substantial unit in plane and solid analytics, for which the students would now be ready.

4.4 Twelfth-Year Mathematics

The twelfth-year course will probably always have two tracks or choices. The main track should probably be the calculus for all mature students. With the background indicated above, there should be absolutely no difficulty; right now, difficulties arise because of the lack of analytic geometry and, in the newer approaches, of linear algebra.

The alternate track (*not* a second track) should probably be a college-preparatory course including such topics as series and sequences, limits, vector and matrix spaces, linear programming and the theory of games, advanced probability, statistics, and FORTRAN. Needless to say, this could be preliminary to engineering, the social sciences or a college course in the calculus.

■ *Andrew M. Gleason*

AXIOMS, POSTULATES, AND THE TEACHING
OF ELEMENTARY MATHEMATICS

Like most controversies, the debate over the use of the axiomatic method in elementary teaching has a considerable semantic component. I do not believe that it is all a question of semantics, but I do believe that it is essential to distinguish various facets of the axiomatic method and to be very explicit about what is intended, for it is not unusual to hear proponents of the axiomatic method urging one thing while the opponents inveigh against another.

To begin with, it is clear that the argument is not over the use of the deductive method. Mathematics is and always will be deductive. The simplest grade school arithmetic problem is an application of the deductive method, for the desired answer is a logical consequence of the hypotheses of the problem. The debate is concerned with what kinds of deductions will be taught, with the level of formality at which they are taught, and with the philosophical attitudes toward the subject as a whole.

The first question to be decided is whether deductions will be kept at the level of individual instances or raised to a level of generality. I was taught the multiplication of integers of several digits by a process which never explicitly left the level of the individual instance. Several examples were worked in detail and explained in terms of what digits were to be multiplied, what carries were to be made, where the results should be written, and what to add to get the final answer. I was left to extract the method by inductive generalization. I was given lots of practice to be sure I had found the method and lots more practice to increase my technical facility. I believe that no statement was ever made which I could now identify as a universally quantified proposition. Before passing on, let me point out that it would be extremely difficult, and certainly inappropriate, to give a description of the multiplication algorithm which could plausibly be interpreted as a universally quantified proposition. "Modern math" programs focus considerable attention on the commutative, associative, and distributive (CAD) laws. They are very explicit that these laws have universal validity within the appropriate number system and they point out how the steps of the multiplication algorithm reflect specializations of these laws. The algorithm itself is taught by instances much the same as before, but the CAD laws help the pupil to see what it is all about. The novelty, insofar as school mathematics is concerned, lies in the fact that universally quantified propositions are explicitly considered and deductions in the form of specializations are recognized.

If we accept the idea that some general propositions should be taught, then we must consider the level of formality at which they should be taught. The suggestion that statements should be presented from the beginning in the technical language of the predicate calculus complete with quantifier symbols can be dismissed. Formal notation adds nothing to the graphic symbolism

$$\square \times (\triangle + \bigcirc) = \square \times \triangle + \square \times \bigcirc$$

together with the purely verbal statement "for any way of filling in the boxes." The essential points are that general statements should be recognized as such and that individual instances should be identified as specializations of the general laws.

One of the arguments over levels of formality seems to concern the use of the words *commutative, associative,* and *distributive.* It is said that these words are too big for children and that their use confuses the issues in verbiage. It is possible, of course, to teach the CAD laws without having names for them, but to do so would be on a par with always referring to Czechoslovakia as "the country between Poland and Austria." No one has ever suggested this or proposed that pupils must learn some new name for the country on the ground that *Czechoslovakia* is too difficult a word. The fact is that children can handle big words and most enjoy learning them. Of course, the words *commutative, associative,* and *distributive,* if indiscriminately bandied about, will confuse the children, but so would *Czechoslovakia* if applied to the wrong country. The argument against the words is specious and only a camouflage for an attack against the laws themselves.

Once quantified statements and deductions from them are accepted, we come to a new question, a purely philosophical question, which is at the very heart of all the controversy over the axiomatic method. What attitude should we take toward the axioms on which we base our mathematics? We may regard the axioms as an effort to set down concisely a description of the facts about numbers or space. Or we may take the axioms as defining the mathematical system which we propose to study. I shall refer to these approaches as *axiomatic* and *postulational* respectively.

The word *axiom* comes from a Greek word meaning to be thought worthy. An axiom is a proposition which is accepted without logical evidence as a basis for logical argument because it is thought worthy, that is, because it appears to be True. In the axiomatic approach to mathematics, we are trying to understand the world about us, possibly the physical world, possibly an idealized world, but in any event a world over which we have no control. Euclid's approach to geometry was axiomatic as is the approach of nearly all elementary geometry texts. The object is to describe, with the aid of a few axioms, the structure of the space in which we live. We accept the axioms of

Euclidean geometry because they accord with our sensory evidence, and if we find that they don't quite make operational sense because of physical limitations, we are prepared to consider an idealized world instead.

The word *postulate* comes from a Latin word meaning to demand. A postulate is a proposition which we demand of the system we are studying. It is really just part of the definition of the system. In the postulational approach to mathematics, we control the system we are studying through our choice of postulates. We are under no obligation to show that our postulates have any relevance to the real world.

Whichever approach we take, the eventual logical situation is the same, but the development is not. The difference is best illustrated by an example. In the postulational approach to arithmetic, we begin by imagining a set of undefined objects endowed with operations called addition and multiplication which satisfy certain conditions, for example, the CAD laws. No effort is made to discuss whether these conditions are met by any system having an *a priori* existence. The mysterious fact that $(-1) \times (-1) = 1$ is a theorem, proved from the postulates by irrefutable logic. Period. In the axiomatic approach, we must face such questions as "What are negative numbers?" and "What does it mean to multiply two negative numbers?" before we can even begin to describe the real number system. Students must be made to sense the value of the concept of negative numbers and they must see that there are significant situations in which we wish to combine two negative numbers to get a positive one and that it is convenient to regard this operation as an extension of multiplication for positive numbers. By the time we write the distributive law as an axiom describing our system, we must have examined enough cases to convince the students that the axiom is reasonable. These cases must involve the multiplication of negative numbers. Hence, we could never accept the distributive law unless we already agreed that $(-1) \times (-1) = 1$. The theorem to this effect, later deduced from the axioms, now acquires a different meaning. It is not new information about the number system but merely confirmation that we have set down the facts correctly. Concomitant with axiomatic mathematics is the realization that we may not have set down the facts correctly. A rethinking of the fundamentals is, therefore, never totally excluded.

A great merit of the axiomatic approach is that it admits the possibility of a mixture of deductive and empirical thinking. Euclidean geometry is notoriously deficient in dealing with the order of points on lines. The remedy, as far as elementary geometry instruction is concerned, is not to introduce half a dozen highly technical axioms for order, but to admit candidly that these questions will be handled by inspecting a carefully drawn figure. This mixed approach is characteristic of all branches of science. Axiomatic mathematics is simply the application of the scientific method to problems classically recognized as purely mathematical.

Modern pure mathematics is always presented from the postulational point of view. Mathematicians make little effort to demonstrate the relevance of their work in terms comprehensible to anyone but an expert. I do not suggest that pure mathematicians give no thought to the relevance of their postulate systems. Quite the contrary, a man's reputation in mathematics is based entirely on the relevance of his research to problems considered important. In spite of appearances, the postulational approach is not actually taken by many mathematicians.

Yet there is a movement which would direct elementary education toward postulationalism. The proponents of this movement do not suggest that we teach irrelevant mathematics. But they fail to appreciate the importance to a beginning student of a justification of the postulate system. In their hurry toward the more sophisticated ways of viewing mathematics, they forget the importance in their own education of the hundreds of examples which, boring as they may have been, did show that mathematics has something to say about the real world.

If mathematics has value, other than pure aesthetics, beyond its practical application, it is because it shows that mental effort can pay off. I suppose this has always been realized by the advocates of mathematics in liberal education, but unfortunately the idea has been hidden behind the puritanical idea of "good mental discipline." I see the current effort to improve the teaching of mathematics largely as a struggle to free the subject from the stultifying force of "mental discipline" so that the student can see the extent to which logical analysis can increase our understanding of the world around us. Unless the connections of mathematics to the real world are kept clearly in sight, we shall relapse into another, more sophisticated, version of mathematics as "mental discipline."

The point of education is to make us all better able to deal with our environment. (I use the word *environment* liberally; I intend to include our personal relations as well as our natural surroundings.) Unfortunately, this principle offers us no real guidance for deciding educational questions. In mathematics it could be used to justify a curriculum devoted to the most practical of applications. But there are long range considerations and it cannot be denied that abstract mathematics has relevance even for computation or that the purest mathematical research has on occasion been of great practical importance.

However, when we consider this principle from the point of view of the student, it acquires a more nearly operational significance. Students measure the value of their own education quite directly in terms of the extent to which it seems to be improving their ability to cope with their environment. Dropouts complain that school had no relevance to their situations. Pupils who come from intellectual backgrounds usually do better at school than those who do not. This is probably because they can see more clearly the relevance of their school work to adult life. The well-known value of games in elementary teaching stems from the same thing. A pupil will work hard to learn what is necessary to compete in a game because success in the game is coping with the environment.

To make education self-motivating, we must arrange that the curriculum is always relevant to the world of the students. At first, the relevance must be immediately apparent. Then, provided the earlier work has been honest and convincing, as the student matures, he will be willing to follow longer trails into unmotivated material if there is a promise of commensurate reward.

In mathematics this means that we must broaden the scope of the curriculum so that the youngest pupils can begin to get a feeling for the possibilities of mathematical analysis. The subject matter must be kept close to applications, but the applications must be carefully chosen to have relevance from the point of view of the child. Organized deductive methods in mathematics should be introduced as soon as they can legitimately contribute to the student's ability to understand and simplify the problems before him. The approach must be axiomatic in the sense I have described above because the overriding consideration is relevance. There is no necessity for completely organized axiom systems as long as we are honest about where we are using deduction and where we are being empirical.

■ *Leon Henkin*

THE AXIOMATIC METHOD IN MATHEMATICS COURSES AT THE SECONDARY LEVEL

I take as an axiom of this paper (if I may begin with a pun) the proposition that the axiomatic method is an important element of contemporary mathematics, both pure and applied, and that the basic ideas involved in this method can be understood by most of our secondary students. From this axiom, together with the fundamental assumptions which underlie our entire educational system, there follows at once the desirability of incorporating a study of the axiomatic method in the secondary curriculum in such a way as to provide an understanding of its character and its function both by students who will be using mathematics as a part of their work and by those who, as "ordinary citizens," should have some appreciation of the basic means by which scientific knowledge is gained and applied.

Since no attempt to justify these presuppositions will be made in this paper, it remains to indicate (a) which aspects of the axiomatic method it is most desirable to bring to the attention of secondary students, and (b) which axiom systems, and which forms of their development, are well suited from the pedagogical viewpoint to illustrate these ideas. In the following two sections of the paper we consider these questions from the perspective of the present level of secondary mathematical education in the United States. In a final section, (c), we deal briefly with variations in the treatment of the axiomatic method which may be anticipated as school mathematical curricula evolve during the coming years.

(a) The most fundamental aspect of the axiomatic method is its role in *organizing* the separate facts of some portion of mathematics or science into a coherent theory by logical derivation of theorems from axioms. Concomitantly an axiomatic development provides an organized structure for the totality of concepts of the theory, through chains of definitions leading from the primitive notions of the system. Although the traditional secondary curriculum does provide some intuitive acquaintance with proofs, the important role of definitions in mathematics is almost totally obscured through two forms of mishandling: furnishing apparent definitions for concepts which are in fact treated thereafter as undefined, and failing to cite definitions at appropriate points of subsequent proofs (often because the definition is not given in a form which makes it usable).

The second most important aspect of the axiomatic method is the possibility of diverse interpretations of the primitive notions of an axiomatized theory, so that investigation of a single system of axioms provides information about a large class of models. This feature of the axiomatic method, unrealized from the time of Euclid up until the last century (and hence excluded from the traditional secondary curriculum), has enormously increased the potential applicability of mathematics and has led mathematicians to perceive and to seek out common elements in seemingly unconnected realms of experience.

At a third level of importance I place the study of isomorphisms, to which the consideration of models of an axiom system naturally leads. This concept is at the root of several divergent paths into domains rich with mathematical ideas, such as automorphism groups, representation theorems, and the formation of homomorphic images, subsystems, and direct products. While most of these areas lie outside the scope of what is feasible in secondary courses at the present time, the concept of isomorphic structures is so central to an understanding of mathematics that it should certainly be included in any study of the axiomatic method.

Finally, after an understanding of the primary mathematical attributes of an axiomatic theory has been achieved, it is time to turn attention to various metamathematical questions. The notions of consistency and satisfiability, independence, completeness and categoricity, and their various interrelationships, are sometimes a little obscure even to the mathematician, but the basic ideas are certainly simple enough for comprehension by the secondary student.

(b) It is a fact familiar enough from the history and practice of mathematics that each new idea is generally discovered in a relatively complicated form, and only subsequently simplified. Such was the case, too, with the discovery of the axiomatic method. From our present perspective, the theory of Euclidean geometry appears to be a particularly clumsy part of mathematics to axiomatize, requiring many axioms and a long, rather computational development from them before the intuitively interesting geometric processes can be studied. What happens in school presentations, of course, is that the passage from axioms to theorems is carried out by means of a generous admixture of geometric intuition to the rules of logical inference, so that the student largely loses this valuable opportunity to sharpen his ideas concerning the laws of logic and the nature of proof.

But there is another reason why Euclidean geometry is poorly suited to introduce the axiomatic method to the young mathematics student, and that is the circumstance that the student at that stage is quite lacking in familiarity with a variety of geometric spaces, so that the notion that there are generally many models for an axiom system can at best be illustrated in a very artificial manner in this context.

It seems clear, by contrast, that an axiomatic theory of one of the familiar number sytems is admirably suited to pedagogical needs: a small number of axioms suffices to characterize any of these sytems; the development leads quickly to the most basic laws; and the students have already become familiar with a variety of systems which can serve as models for the axiom set (and various of its subsets). The way in which such a theory can serve to exemplify these aspects of the axiomatic method which were enumerated in Section (a) above, is indicated better by illustration than by description. Accordingly, we outline below an abbreviated presentation of an axiomatic theory of positive rational numbers, suitable for study at the secondary level. Our emphasis will be on introductory and explanatory remarks; all proofs will be omitted. At the end of the presentation we shall call attention to several of its features which are especially relevant for pedagogical purposes.

By a *number system* we shall understand a system consisting of a nonempty set of elements together with two binary operations on it. (A binary operation on a set can be applied to any pair of elements of the set—in a given order— the result of the application being again an element of the set.) Of course we are familiar with various number systems from our early studies in elementary school.

The simplest number system, and the one about which we learn first, consists of the counting numbers (or positive integers), 1, 2, 3, . . . , with the usual operations of addition and multiplication on them. Later we enlarge this number system by adding successively the number 0, the fractional numbers (or ratios of positive integers), the negative numbers, and still other numbers such as $\sqrt{2}$ and π. The positive and negative fractional numbers, together with zero, are called *rational numbers,* and the set R of all these numbers, together with the addition and multiplication operations on them, form a number system (for when we add or multiply two rational numbers, the result is again such a number—in other words, R is *closed* under $+$ and $\cdot$). We call $(R, +, \cdot)$ *the rational number system.*

Why do we pass from the system of positive integers to that of rational numbers? From the viewpoint of *applications* we need the new numbers when we pass from counting problems to such problems as measuring, dividing, and locating. From the viewpoint of *pure* mathematics the new system has certain desirable properties which were lacking in the original system, and among these is *solvability of equations.* In both systems we find that certain laws hold, such as the commutative, associative, and distributive laws, which express a regularity about the operations of addition and multiplication. However, the sentence "Given any numbers a and b there is a number x such that $a + x = b$" holds for the system of rational numbers, but it does not hold for the system of positive integers. In the latter system it is true for *certain* numbers a and b that there is a number x such that $a + x = b$ (namely, for those numbers a and b such that $a < b$), but for other positive integers a and b there is *no* such positive integer x. Also in the case of multiplicative equations, $a \cdot x = b$, many are solvable and many are unsolvable in the system of positive integers, while in the system of rational numbers all are solvable except for the case where $a = 0$ and $b \neq 0$. Of course we may consider this exceptional case an undesirable irregularity, and we may seek some other number system in which all multiplicative equations without exception are solvable. Actually there *is* a number system in which the commutative, associative, and distributive laws hold, and in which all additive and multiplicative equations are solvable, but this system contains only one number—can you guess which it is? It can be demonstrated, however, that there cannot be such a system which contains the positive integers among its numbers.

Between the systems of positive integers and of rational numbers lie two others—the system of all integers (positive, negative, and zero), in which additive but not all multiplicative equations are solvable, and the system of all positive rational numbers in which multiplicative but not all additive equations are solvable. We are now going to investigate the latter system, developing its theory by the axiomatic method.

What does this mean? The basic idea is that we shall show that the various facts about this system which we have come to know through our earlier studies are related to one another. We shall show this by choosing certain facts and calling them *axioms*, and then by deriving all of the other facts from these. Our method of derivation will be to employ the rules of *logic;* even though we have not studied these rules explicitly, we shall find that they are intuitively familiar to us because their validity depends on the meanings of simple words which we have used all during our lives. In addition to showing how facts are related to each other, the axiomatic method exhibits the relations which exist among the various concepts involved in our number system by showing how many of them can be defined in terms of others; those concepts which lie at the starting point of our series of definitions are called the *primitive* (or undefined) notions of the theory.

The fact that our axioms are not proved in the theory does not mean that they are intrinsically unprovable—only that, since we must start *somewhere*, we will use these assertions as the basis of our proofs *for this axiom system.* Similarly, there is nothing intrinsically undefinable about our primitive notions—we just decide to use these as the starting point for our definitions *in this theory.* The question of how we select these axioms and primitive notions will be discussed later; at the moment we shall merely stress that an entirely equivalent and fully satisfactory theory of positive integers could start with different primitives and axioms, and in that theory *our* primitive notions would be defined, and *our* axioms would be stated as theorems and proved.

The *primitive notions* of our theory will be *positive rational number* (referred to hereafter as *number* for short), *addition*, and *multiplication*. We use "*P*" as a name for the set of all numbers, "$+$" as a name for addition, and "$\cdot$" as a name for multiplication.

Axiom (i). The system $(P, +, \cdot)$ is a number system; that is, the set P is nonempty and $+$ and $\cdot$ are binary operations on P. (Note that we do not specify which elements are in the set P, and we do not specify which binary operations $+$ and $\cdot$ are, so this is not a definition. It is true that the term "positive rational number" and the symbols "$+$" and "$\cdot$" are used ordinarily for special objects and particular operations, but we shall never make use of these ordinary meanings in developing our axiomatic theory by definitions and by proofs of theorems.)

Axiom (ii). For all x, y, z in P we have $(x + y) + z = x + (y + z)$ and $(x \cdot y) \cdot z = x \cdot (y \cdot z)$. (These are the familiar *associative laws* for $+$ and $\cdot$ respectively.)

Axiom (iii). For all x, y, z in P we have $x \cdot (y + z) = (x \cdot y) + (x \cdot z)$ and $(y + z) \cdot x = (y \cdot x) + (z \cdot x)$. (These are the familiar *distributive laws* of $\cdot$ over $+$. Of course the second one follows easily from the first if we use the commutative law of multiplication, but we shall not be taking the latter as an axiom, so we use both distributive laws among our axioms; we shall see that they both play a role when we come to *prove* the commutative law of multiplication as a *theorem*.)

Axiom (iv). For all a, b in P there is an x in P such that $a \cdot x = b$ and there is a y in P such that $y \cdot a = b$. (The axioms express the solvability of all multiplicative equations in the system of positive rational numbers; there are no exceptional cases since there is no number 0 in this system.)

Axioms (v), *(vi)*, *(vii)*. We shall defer the formulation of the final three axioms until we have begun to develop the system from *Axioms (i)–(iv)*.

Theorem 1. There is one and only one number a in P such that $a \cdot x = x$ for *every* x in P; furthermore, for this number a we have also $x \cdot a = x$ for all x in P.

Now that we know there is exactly one element of P having a certain property, we are entitled to introduce a special name for that element. We do this by a definition.

Definition A. We define 1 to be the unique element described in Theorem 1. (Thus we have $1 \cdot x = x$ and $x \cdot 1 = x$ for all x in P.)

Theorem 2. For *each* element a in P there is one and only one element x in P such that $a \cdot x = 1$; furthermore, for this element x we have also $x \cdot a = 1$.

Definition B. For any element a in P we let a^{-1} be the unique element of P such that $a \cdot a^{-1} = 1$ and $a^{-1} \cdot a = 1$.

53

Theorem 3. For all x and y in P we have $(x^{-1})^{-1} = x$ and $(x \cdot y)^{-1} = y^{-1} \cdot x^{-1}$.

Definition C. For any x, y in P we let x/y be the element $x \cdot y^{-1}$.

Theorem 4. For all x, y, z in P we have: $x/x = 1$, $(x/y)^{-1} = y/x$, $(x \cdot z)/(y \cdot z) = x/y$, $(x/y) \cdot (y/z) = x/z$, $x/z + y/z = (x + y)/z$.

It will be seen from this theorem that many of the familiar rules for computing with fractions can be derived in a purely logical manner from *Axioms* (i)–(iv); nevertheless, the basic rule for addition, $(x/u) + (y/v) = (x \cdot v + u \cdot y)/(u \cdot v)$ *cannot* be proved in this way. We shall see later how we can actually demonstrate such an unprovability fact; meanwhile, in order to be able to derive the basic rule for adding fractions in our system, we introduce our fifth axiom.

Axiom (v). If G is any nonempty subset of P which is closed under the operations $+$ and $/$ (i.e., such that whenever x, y are in P we also have $x + y$ and x/y in P), then $G = P$.

This axiom looks very different from the ones introduced heretofore. From the technical viewpoint it contains the variable "G" which ranges over subsets of P, where as the earlier axioms contained only variables like "x" and "a" which range over elements of P. We express this by saying that *Axiom* (v) is a *second order* sentence while the others are *first order;* in advanced studies it can be shown that it is impossible to have an adequate system of axioms for the system of positive rational numbers if we use *only* first order axioms.

Another difference between *Axiom* (v) and the earlier ones, non-technical in nature, is that Axioms (i)–(iv) were familiar to us, and known to be true from our intuitive acquaintance with the positive rational numbers, whereas *Axiom* (v) is not. Of course we cannot ask for a proof of this proposition within our axiom system, since we are taking it as an axiom; but we *would* like to feel convinced that it is true before being willing to work with it as an axiom. Here is an intuitive argument which may convince you.

Take any nonempty set G of positive rational numbers which is closed under $+$ and $/$. Choose a number a in G; then a/a is in G, i.e., $1 \in G$. Hence $1 + 1$, or 2, is in G; hence $2 + 1$, or 3, is in G. Continuing in this way we see that every positive integer is in G. But then, since G is closed under $/$, every positive rational will also be in G.

Let us repeat that this argument does not pretend to be a proof; the phrase "continuing in this way . . . ," especially when we know it covers infinitely many steps, is too vague to be allowed to stand as part of a mathematical proof. Nevertheless the argument will probably be convincing enough intuitively to justify our use of *Axiom* (v). Now let us see what we can do with it.

Theorem 5. For all x, y in P, $x \cdot y = y \cdot x$.

With the commutative law of multiplication at hand we can go back to the material based on *Axioms (i)–(iv)* and complete the basic rules for computing with fractions.

Theorem 6. For all x, y, u, v in P we have: $(x/u) \cdot (y/v) = (x \cdot y) / (u \cdot v)$, $(x/u) / (y/v) = (x \cdot v) / (y \cdot u)$, $(x/u) + (y/v) = (x \cdot v + u \cdot y) / (u \cdot v)$, $x/u = y/v$ if and only if $x \cdot v = u \cdot y$.

In order to obtain the commutative law of addition we need our sixth axiom, a special case of the cancellation law for addition (which implies the general law).

Axiom (vi). For any x, y in P such that $x + 1 = y + 1$ we have $x = y$.

Theorem 7. If x, y, z are any elements of P such that $x + z = y + z$, then $x = y$.

Theorem 8. For all x, y in P, $x + y = y + x$.

So far all of the theorems we have proved are in the form of general laws which hold for all elements of P. Can we prove facts about individual numbers, say that $1 + 1 \neq 1$? We certainly would like to, if we are developing a full theory of positive rational numbers; yet this particular fact can*not* be proven from *Axioms (i)–(vi)* alone. The impossibility of such a proof is not a theorem of our axiomatic theory, but is a result *about* this theory; such a result we call a *metatheorem*.

Metatheorem I. In the system of *Axioms (i)–(vi)* it is impossible to prove that $1 + 1 \neq 1$.

The need for an additional axiom is now clear. Here is our last one.

Axiom (vii). There exist numbers x, y in P such that $x \neq y$.

Theorem 9. For all x, y in P, $x + y \neq x$.

Space does not permit the further outline of the development of this axiomatic system; suffice it to say that we are at the stage where the positive integers are introduced by definition, and the metatheorem that any two number systems satisfying *Axioms (i)–(vii)* must be isomorphic then quickly follows. The discussion of the significance of this result provides an opportunity for introducing such metamathematical concepts as completeness and consistency.

It is worthwhile noticing how, in the introductory remarks of this axiomatic theory, the motivation for *Axiom (iv)* is planted and how by introducing the general term "number system" the ground is laid for later consideration of various models of fragments of the axiom system.

Our experience suggests that the *first* explanation of the purpose of axiomatization should be limited to the desire to study the logical relations among mathematical propositions holding in a given structure, with the question of self-evidence handled in an incidental way (as in our discussion of *Axiom (v)* above). Only later should the applicability of given axioms to a variety of models be brought out. The latter concept is more meaningful to the student after he has actually worked a while with logical derivations; the delay also provides an element of dramatic impact which is valuable in maintaining and enlarging the student's interest in the work.

It is to be emphasized that a thorough understanding of the axiomatic method cannot be achieved if the student's study is limited to deriving theorems within a given axiom system. He should also be asked to find definitions. Furthermore, after working through the development of *given* axioms he should be asked to *construct* an axiom system for some other theory. (For example, an axiomatic theory of the integers is a natural counterpart to the system given above.) Discussion of the considerations affecting the construction of a set of axioms gives opportunity for considering a host of fruitful concepts—including questions of mathematical esthetics.

(c) The program discussed above can be profitably carried through in average high school classes today during a second year of algebra. As with other truly fundamental concepts, however, we should look toward a future development of the curriculum in which at least rudimentary forms of the axiomatic method appear early in the *elementary* curriculum, reappearing in increasingly significant forms through the grades. When such an elementary curriculum has been achieved the secondary student will require a more sophisticated treatment of the axiomatic method than the one we have outlined.

One possible direction would consist in allocating to the secondary schools responsibility for a complete and thorough treatment of the real number system. This would involve axiomatic treatments of the natural numbers, the rationals, and the reals, as well as definitional constructions of each of the latter systems on the base of its predecessor system. Such dual treatments have several advantages: the construction provides a relative consistency proof of the axiomatic version, and the axiom system shows what are the essential properties of the construction.

Another direction for deepening an understanding of the axiomatic method after a suitable groundwork has been laid in elementary school would consist of an axiomatization of the algebra of sets, leading through Boolean algebras to a general introduction to representation theorems and their significance.

■ *Morris Kline*

MATHEMATICS AND AXIOMATICS

Deductive mathematics, fashioned by the classical Greeks, was transmitted to us through such significant works as Euclid's *Elements* and Apollonius' *Conic Sections*. Though these creations were an intellectual blessing to humanity, it was a pedagogical calamity that only such books survived as the representatives of Greek mathematical activity. The impression gained by the succeeding generations was that the essence of mathematics consisted of axiomatics; that is, one started with axioms and then proved theorems in a rigid deductive sequence. This superficial and largely erroneous view of mathematics has become especially popular in our generation. The late nineteenth-century efforts to repair in Euclid's system of axioms the defects that had been uncovered by the work in non-Euclidean geometry and the efforts to supply a logical basis for the real number system strengthened the belief that mathematics means axiomatics.

Had other works of the classical Greek period survived, the Western world would surely have gotten a better understanding of the true nature of mathematics. The Greeks did possess it. They knew that conjectures must precede proofs and that analysis precedes synthesis. For example, Proclus, the famous fifth-century commentator on Euclid, says "it is . . . necessary to know beforehand what is sought." In fact the Greeks did not think much of propositions which fell out readily and quickly by more or less obvious deductions from the axioms and the preceding theorems. These they called porisms or corollaries. To divine the significant theorem and to devise the proof, these were the challenges and the meaningful activity. Of course it is not necessary to have recourse to the more esoteric history of Greek mathematics to appreciate that mathematics is not synonymous with axiomatics. We have only to look at the development of mathematics from 1500 on. The greatest creations since that time have been in the fields of algebra and analysis and these subjects had no axiomatic basis until about 1900.

Even a student who attempts an original exercise knows how much floundering, conjecturing, and trial and error are needed to obtain the proof despite the fact that the axiomatic basis and the statement to be proved are at hand. How much more creating and thinking must be involved before one chooses the axioms and knows what to prove? The creative process, then, which constitutes by far the largest and the most difficult part of mathematical activity, is not contained in the axiomatic approach.

Moreover in seeking theorems, what directions or goals does mathematical thinking pursue? Do we just prove what comes to mind or what can be proved readily? Such a development would be inane. There is the possibility that esthetic standards might direct the choice but taste is personal and therefore also controversial. Whatever determines the goals of mathematical activity, certainly the axiomatic presentation says nothing about them and in fact suggests that we can have no goals because what we prove must follow from the axioms.

Even if instruction in mathematics is intended merely to transmit knowledge, the totally deductive presentation gives no insight into what is accomplished. It is the finished structure with all the scaffolding removed, as Gauss once remarked, and it is usually so much prettied up that one doesn't see the framework. In other words, the ideas underlying a proof are difficult to discern in the stilted deductive formulation. In particular, the axiomatic basis for the real number system is a totally artificial creation which satisfied a purely professional objective, to supply a logical basis for what we already knew. One does not use it in the subsequent development of mathematics or in applying mathematics, nor was it intended for these purposes. One of our best professors once remarked that when as a student he learned the axiomatic approach to the real number system, he concluded that the entities and properties so established could never be useful.

The argument against overemphasis on axiomatization and deductive proof can be based on even deeper considerations. The modern mathematics movement, insofar as it emphasizes rigorous axiomatics, reflects most directly the mathematicians' concern of the early 1900's. But since that time the discovery of the difficulties in the foundations of mathematics has thrown open the entire question of what mathematics is. The most pertinent result, insofar as there are results, is that which follows from Gödel's theorem: no significant branch of mathematics can be encompassed in an axiomatic approach. What also seems to be indicated is that mathematics rests on intuitions and that proof can be no more than the hygiene, which as Herman Weyl remarked, merely keeps the ideas of mathematics healthy and strong. The eighteenth-century empirical mathematicians may have had the far wiser philosophy than that which those of us educated in the tradition of Bolzano, Cauchy and Weierstrass have been led to accept.

In short, the axiomatic, deductive approach to mathematics omits the creative process, is often contrived, and is obscure. Exclusive use of it or even emphasis on it can be disastrous, especially for the training of mathematicians. The axiomatic method is just one element in mathematics and a subordinate element at that. It is true that logical proof is a standard and an obligation of mathematics, but, as Jacques Hadamard remarked, it merely sanctions the conquests of the intuition. The vital mathematics is the creative activity which becomes a re-creative activity for students. The mathematical activity proper consists not in agreeing to someone else's thinking but in thinking for oneself, which means guessing, conjecturing, blundering, trial and error, induction from concrete evidence and all the other diverse and often haphazard processes which enter into thinking. Creativity presupposes flexibility in solving problems and any ideas from any domain of mathematics that seem promising should be entertained whether or not they fall within the confines of a particular axiomatic structure. The latter, in fact, acts as a straitjacket on the mind. Moreover, mathematics serves purposes, notably to cooperate with science in the common effort to understand and master the physical world. The more immediate goals in a branch whose structure is already established may be purely mathematical such as generalization and abstraction, but one must never lose sight of the larger objectives. To understand and pursue these intelligently is also part of mathematics.

It is agreed, however, that the axiomatization of any branch of mathematics is a phase, even if subordinate, of mathematical activity. It is a check on the thinking and a systematic organization of the knowledge gained. How much should we do with it? In other words, how completely or how rigorously can one present the axiomatic approach to high school and college students? Here pedagogy rather than *a priori* consideration dictates what we must do. It is first necessary to be clear that young people will see the point of a proof only if it proves what is not obvious on the basis of what is obvious. To prove that a line segment has a unique midpoint is to confuse the student about the purpose of proof, as well as about the very nature of mathematics. To introduce axioms such as the order or betweeness axioms in geometry is to ask students to accept as necessary what does not seem at all necessary to them. Moreover, since these axioms are sophisticated and the student does not grasp their significance, he cannot think about them and use them in proofs. The capacity to appreciate rigor is a function of the mathematical age of the student and not of the age of mathematics. This appreciation must be acquired gradually and the students must have the same freedom to make mistakes that the mathematicians had. Rigor will not refine an intuition which has not been allowed to function freely.

Of course the dictates of pedagogy conflict sharply with the interests and standards of the professional mathematician. He wants to give students the whole "truth" at once so that they should not have to unlearn what they have once learned. But one cannot teach even history or Shakespeare in this way. Moreover, the mathematician wishes to have not only a complete set of axioms but a minimum number and, in a logical sense, simple axioms. He also wishes to have independent axioms. These conditions on, or properties of, axiom systems must be sacrificed in behalf of pedagogy. Even if such systems

59

could be made understandable to young people, the time required to teach them could be spent on more significant material. To teach rigorous axiomatic developments to young people is an abuse of pedagogy.

As a matter of fact the attempt to be completely deductive ensnares the mathematician in a trap. It is often necessary to present a proof which is too difficult for the student, such as the proof of the formula for the area of a circle in plane geometry. The deductively oriented mathematician evades the pedagogical problem by adopting an axiom. As a consequence numerous standard elementary geometry texts now contain as many as 70 or 80 axioms. Surely if one can adopt axioms at will (within the limitation of consistency), there is no need to prove anything. The mathematics teacher can no more afford to be profligate with axioms than to be parsimonious.

The axioms should be obvious to the student and this implies that they must conform to and be based on his experiences in the real world. However, even here we must be careful. It is true that the commutative and associative properties of whole numbers and fractions are familiar to the student on the basis of his experience in handling collections and parts of objects. But the student is so familiar with these properties that he does not realize he is using them. He does not question them any more than he does the fact that a line segment has a midpoint. Because these properties are ingrained, it is better not to make them explicit not only for the reason already given, that this would confuse the student about proof, but because to ask students to use them explicitly is impractical. For if one uses such axioms to justify every step that is involved in showing, for example, that $3ab\,(ab + 2ac) = 3a^2b^2 + 9a^2bc$, he will require an interminable amount of time to do even the simplest algebra. We should be grateful that the students accept such facts without question, and, in fact, do all we can to make the elementary operations so habitual that one does not have to think about them at all, any more than one thinks when he ties his shoelaces. If students do not see readily that $3x = x \cdot 3$, it is not because they lack familiarity with the commutative principle, but rather because they fail to understand that x is just a number (or, more properly these days, a placeholder for the name of a number). Those who are concerned that commutativity may become so inbred that students will refuse to multiply matrices are not only needlessly fearful but are trying to rush the educational process.

The need to make some of the work automatic is stressed by a man who certainly understood the role of axiomatics, Alfred North Whitehead. In his *An Introduction to Mathematics* (p. 61) he says: "It is a profoundly erroneous truism, repeated by all copy-books and by eminent people when they are making speeches, that we should cultivate the habit of thinking of what we are doing. The precise opposite is the case. Civilization advances by extending the number of important operations which we can perform without thinking

60

about them. Operations of thought are like cavalry charges in a battle—they are strictly limited in number, they require fresh horses, and must only be made at decisive moments."

Despite these cautions about going too far with the details of the axiomatic phase of mathematics education, it must be admitted that the traditional curricula have been inconsistent. Euclidean geometry has been presented deductively but algebra has been presented mechanically as a series of techniques. Surely if both are part of mathematics, the differences in presentation must have been confusing to the students, though they may not have been aware of the source of their confusion. The existence of these differences over many centuries demonstrates that the kind of mathematics education we have been giving does not train even mathematicians to think. The inconsistency in the traditional presentation of these two subjects should certainly have struck teachers of mathematics one hundred years ago. Historically one can understand how this inconsistency arose. Euclidean geometry, as we have already noted, was acquired by Western civilization in the organized, deductive form whereas algebra grew up as an empirical science, with no rigorous logical foundation until about 1900. However, it would have been possible to give a deductive organization on the level of Euclid's rigor even in 1850. As a matter of fact George Peacock and Augustus De Morgan did so.

The proper reform should certainly uniformize the treatment of the two subjects. This reform involves a two-fold change. Some deductive structure should be introduced in algebra but by no means a rigorous one. Axioms such as equals added to equals and the like can certainly be used to accustom students to the idea of proof. On the other hand, we must add especially to the geometry, but also to the algebra, the motivated, constructive approach which will permit students to see why we investigate topics such as congruence and why we seek to establish particular theorems and which will enable them to take part in fashioning theorems and proofs. The insight which this approach to geometry and to algebra affords has been denied to the student, and the impression given in geometry is that the theorems flow inevitably and invariably from the axioms.

We do not seem to recognize or admit that students have the right to question why we establish particular theorems or techniques. The student who complains, "Who cares whether the altitudes of a triangle meet in a point?", is wiser than the one who passively memorizes the proof and hands it back on an examination. Mathematicians have felt free to discard whole branches of their subject on the ground that they are no longer of interest, but see no inconsistency in denying to the young student, who as yet has no love for any kind of mathematics, the motivation for studying particular theorems or techniques.

Despite all of the arguments against overemphasis of axiomatics, arguments

61

which stem from the nature of mathematical activity, the current understanding (or lack of understanding) of the proper foundations of mathematics, and pedagogy, the trend today on all levels of mathematics education is to teach axiomatically. Why is the axiomatic approach so popular? The answer seems to be that it is the easy way out. Hardly any work is required to present axioms and their consequences in the approved fashion. One merely repeats the steps and the reasons. On the other hand, to know why a theorem should be proved at all, to penetrate to the basic idea of the proof, and to know why one proof is preferable to another or why one order of theorems rather than another is necessary calls first of all for a depth of understanding. Moreover, having acquired the understanding, it is far more difficult to present the mathematics so that the students take part in the divination of theorems and proofs and then in the casting of these discoveries into the axiomatic mold. To state it otherwise, to motivate and to teach discovery are difficult tasks and require much thought and preparation. It is far easier to take the position which Samuel Johnson once adopted when he refused to explain further something he had said: "I have found you an argument, but I am not obliged to find you an understanding."

■ *Merrill E. Shanks*

THE AXIOMATIC METHOD AND SCHOOL MATHEMATICS

There are two principal ways in which axiomatics relate to the schools. The first of these is the direct use of the axiomatic method in the classroom. Here the text is arranged deductively: axioms, definitions, and theorems follow one another, presumably with all the steps included. The second way in which axiomatics has an impact is through the author's awareness (or unawareness) of an underlying axiomatic development that can guide his preparation of a syllabus or a textbook. Here the text is arranged to conform to a *possible* deductive development but can be much sketchier. I shall comment on both these aspects in turn. My comments will apply only to past and present practices in the United States, though I doubt not that similar observations can be made in part about other countries.

The Recent Past

Before getting to the specific point of contention, consider briefly the historical origins of our current revolution in school mathematics—at least insofar as it is caused by, or related to, axiomatics. The traditional spot in the curriculum for deductive mathematics has for years been 10th grade geometry. This course grew over the years, influenced by "progressive education" and the vastly expanded educational base, into a diluted and confused version of Euclid's *Elements*. One might have expected the opposite reaction to the elucidation, around the turn of the century, of adequate foundations for Euclidean geometry. Instead, there was a retreat from rigor. Texts were written by persons either inadequately trained in, or insensitive to, precision and elegance in mathematics. Moreover, the research mathematicians with few exceptions remained unconcerned with school matters.

There were several serious objections to this state of affairs. In the first place, to render the subject "easier," authors inserted additional "axioms" which were often a positive hindrance to an understanding of geometry. Some of these "axioms" were simply definitions; others were easy theorems; occasionally one was false! Speaking personally, one of the strongest incentives for writing school mathematics has been a desire to excise from the syllabus these false, excessively redundant, and misleading aspects. This pseudo-mathematics of traditional geometry was objectionable in many ways. One was that it fostered a tendency to rote learning and memorization. Ritual memorization of proofs was often the only way for a teacher, or thoughtful student, to wade through the mish-mash that purported to be deductive. Artificial "reasoning" could, and did, repel able students. Really perceptive minds, if they read all the nonsense in these texts, might very well conclude that mathematics is absurd. To exite a student about geometry a teacher had to push quickly through the weak foundations to get to the firmer ground of interesting applications of the basic theorems. So it was that there was reason to hear the cry, "Away with axiomatics!"—whereas, the proper slogan should be, "Away with *bad* axiomatics!"—and also, away with axiomatics that requires extensive memorization before lending excitement.

I wish to make a case for the use of the *axiomatic method in the classroom* without the reader being prejudiced by what has passed for axiomatics in the past. Now, by "axiomatics in the classroom," I mean teaching, *at least part of the time*, rigorous deduction from precisely stated, and mathematically adequate, assumptions. Observe that I do not say this aspect is all of the syllabus. Neither do I say that the assumptions are minimal. In school mathematics a certain degree of repetition in the axiom structure is both necessary and desirable.

Another, but possibly the least essential, objection to traditional geometry was that it did not provide an adequate foundation for geometry. Means to remedy the logical deficiencies of Euclid have been known since the turn of the century. Yet these significant advances in our understanding of geometry have had, until recently, no impact on school geometry.

So, to summarize, until recently we had corrupt axiom systems that were mathematically inadequate which were taught all too often in an unimaginative and uncompromising way. The time was ripe for a revolution.

The Present

Let me turn now to the current state of affairs. During the past ten or twelve years we have seen much precise mathematics taught to young people. An existence theorem has been established to the effect that sound, rigorous mathematics can be taught with mutual enjoyment of teacher and pupil. It is no longer possible to contend that one cannot teach deductive mathematics in the schools. The argument now takes the form, "Should one axiomatize?" And even this question is not really in dispute. No one I know advocates complete absence of deductive argument from clearly stated assumptions. The real questions therefore seem to be these:

What should one axiomatize?

When should one begin to axiomatize?

How should one proceed? By this I mean technical questions relating to pedagogically optimum choices of axiom systems.

And finally, *balance*. To what extent is the pupil to be conscious of the inexorable development of structure? Does axiomatics play a dominant or subservient role?

Let me say at once that I do not think there are definitive answers to these questions, and certainly not ones which all mathematicians will find equally palatable. Even the atoms of Bourbaki do not always vibrate in unison. Different countries, different school populations and environments, and different temperaments will dictate differing answers. Moreover, the teacher still plays the dominant role. He can either reinforce or distort the aims of the best designed syllabus.

Some Opinions

To limit the discussion, I shall consider only the so-called college capable pupil, although most of what I say is applicable, at a slower pace and at a higher age level, to weaker students.

My major claim for good axiomatics in the classroom is that students actually thrive on it. Thorough attention to careful argument becomes a game to young minds. They enjoy seeing underlying reasons and they relish catching a classmate, or better the teacher, in a lapse. I firmly believe the following:

(a) A pupil should never be allowed to get away with sloppy argument. And he should be pushed to explain himself at every opportunity. Naturally, this does not mean repetition of ritual phrases from the text.

(b) To create independent minds there is nothing better than to create critical minds, and axiomatics helps do this. I recall hearing of a student who after a year of axiomatic algebra began a traditional geometry course. There he encountered, "The whole is equal to the sum of its parts and greater than any part." He told his teacher this was false and gave this proof:

$$-10 = (-7) + (-3), \text{ so } -7 \text{ is a part of } -10, \text{ yet } -7 > -10!$$

(c) Axiomatic detail need not be deadly. I recall a selected class discussing *extemporaneously* and with keen interest a proof that a ray with endpoint in the interior of a triangle must meet the triangle.

As another example, there is the 11th grade pupil who, with some outside reading, made up an axiom system of his own for plane geometry.

(d) Axiomatics can lessen the fear of not "knowing." Emphasis on deduction tends to lend assurance that one can always draw *some* positive conclusions. The student is more inclined to search than to memorize procedures.

(e) Student "discovery" is just as much present with the axiomatic method as it is in free exploration or in problem solving. Possibly different sorts of discovery occur, but they do occur. There is the example of the pupil who had been confused about a proof (not the fact, only the proof) that: $a - (b - c) = (a + c) - b$. Later, on meeting and proving the analogue: $a/(b/c) = ac/b$, his reaction was pleasure in observing that he now understood the earlier subtraction problem and that the two problems were "essentially" the same.

(f) To foster independence of mind in young students is surely a worthwhile endeavor, but independence without respect for premises is anarchy. Axiomatics does foster respect for premises and moreover generates an appreciation for the mutual relations of axiom and theorem—that there is a measure of artistic choice as to which comes first.

I have been discussing the insight gained by the student into the logical relations in elementary mathematics, an insight that is encouraged through use of the axiomatic method. Moreover, at the same time the pupil obtains a glimpse into the creation of larger, more elaborate mathematical systems from simpler ones. But this is not the whole story. Besides this structural and logical aspect of mathematics, there are the two other aspects of school mathematics. First, there is the matter of technical skill, of algorithmic competence, of computation. No program of instruction is viable that allows the pupil to push on without this competence. This is the analogue of practicing scales on the piano, though one tries to obtain this skill while doing interesting problems. Second, there is the matter of applications. Here are included both "story" problems and genuine applications to science. It has been said that the newer curricula have paid inadequate attention to these aspects of computation and application. At times, in this period of change, this may indeed be true, but such deficiencies, if they exist, should not affect one's judgment about using the axiomatic method. The issue is too important to allow slogans or polemics to be decisive. Incidentally, I must mention that one of the serious difficulties in applying mathematics to science is that *the science* (school science, that is) *is not axiomatic enough.*

Finally, in defense of the axiomatic method, I remark that, as practiced by the better teachers, there is freedom *not* to prove every last item. A good student should be (and most will be) content to reach a position from which easy, obvious theorems can be taken for granted. He should feel happy with statements like this, "One can prove . . . without trouble." Only a confirmed skeptic needs to supply every detail. When obvious theorems seem to be provable (and if indeed they actually are), then one should push on to less obvious matters.

The Near Future in the United States

People in other countries often do not realize the tremendous variety in our schools. There is no federally imposed norm for educational standards and so one finds astonishingly good ones and astonishingly poor ones, with most of them in a state of uninspiring mediocrity. Now with the revival of general interest in educational matters and in particular the revolution in school mathematics, we have reached a period of consolidation after great progress. The impact of the new curricula, in particular that of the School Mathematics Study Group, has been to bring rigorous mathematics down into grades below the tenth and at the same time to render it *fashionable!* All the new curricula are far more axiomatic than those in the past. Consequently, regardless of the exact direction that we take now, there is no question but that the axiomatic method will occupy a more central position than before. Our immediate problem therefore turns out to be the training and the retraining of teachers competent to teach deductive mathematics with enjoyment.

While we work at the problem of teacher competence, the use of the new materials will bring to light weaknesses and suggest new directions to take. Yet while consolidation takes place in practice, new experiments and new materials are under development. This brings up the next aspect to be discussed.

Axiomatics and the Writing of Textbooks

As a final argument in favor of the increased use of the axiomatic method, I take note of the salutary effect it can have in the planning, and writing, of new books. The thesis is simple enough: to write with a specific axiom system firmly in mind can provide an author with reasons for selecting the topics discussed, the order in which they should appear, and the manner in which they should be explained.

Too often in the past it appears that authors* have written with the sole objective of teaching a few rote responses by providing teacher and student with "activities" to fill the class hour. It is instructive, and disheartening, to read through many school texts and fail to find any march of ideas. Instead one can find errors, lacunae, iteration of the obvious, trivia, and failure to exploit ideas that have been discussed. During the past year I have examined, with a critical eye, some of our widely used books. Almost without exception they would gain in clarity and teachability if they were presented with a clearly conceived axiomatic basis in mind. That there is great variety in these books is not bad. In the United States we need this variety. Nor is it bad that many problems are ridiculously easy; weak students need easy problems. What is bad is that books with bad axiomatics (or none) underlying their exposition are likely to give a completely false idea of what mathematics is really like.

Let it be clear. I am *not* talking about explicit use of the axiomatic method in classes. What I am saying is that authors must know the ground on which they walk, and that the student will then find it easier to learn. Explanations then flow more naturally; they are less ad hoc. Here are a few questions that can arise, at various levels, and which are much easier to attack when one has a definite *mathematical* point of view. I do not say that axiomatics alone can answer these questions. It is necessary but not sufficient. There are pedagogical questions, too, and matters of expedience in dealing with applications.

(1) In the early grades: If whole numbers are cardinal numbers of finite sets,

---

* I speak of authors of American texts but there are other examples. However, it is different in many countries because the practice has been for school texts to be written by working mathematicians. In such cases it is often clearer that the author had a particular mathematical point of view.

does counting come before or after addition? If you count first, is not addition already present?

Do you regard multiplication as repeated addition or get it from Cartesian products? Evidently the discussion of the distributive law, among other things, may differ in the two cases.

(2) In the middle grades: What is a rational number? If equivalence of fractions is to lead to rational numbers, is the discussion of equivalence to be based on consideration of finite sets or on purely arithmetic considerations? One can proceed either way but he must know what has been done in order to tell a theorem from a definition.

(3) In the junior high school: What is a real number? Today all texts, if they come to the real numbers at all, base their exposition on decimals. Someone should try something new.

Should deduction begin in grade 7? Earlier? Later? Should not the algebraic and geometric basis here be the same as that used in the, presumably, more deductive development in grades 9 and up?

(4) In the high school: Should deductive Euclidean geometry be isolated in the tenth grade? Should it be taught at all? Should we not teach deductive algebra and deductive geometry *concurrently* whenever we decide to be deductive? In this last event, where algebra and geometry are concurrent, that is cotemporal, presumably each would have a separate axiomatic basis, and they would not intermingle extensively till later on. With this kind of axiomatic development, not all sets of axioms for geometry are equally effective. Are there attractive alternatives to what we are doing now?

In conclusion, let me say this. In the United States we have in the recent past made a significant advance toward sound, exciting mathematics in the schools. To a great extent this advance has been based on use of the axiomatic method in the classroom. It is hard to see how in the future there will be less axiomatics. Rather, it seems to me that we shall see a more unified treatment and a better coordination of the axioms with computational algorithms and with the applications.

■ *Patrick Suppes*

THE AXIOMATIC METHOD IN HIGH SCHOOL MATHEMATICS

Introduction. The importance of the axiomatic method in modern mathematics scarcely needs a general defense. Its widespread use in many parts of mathematics and its long history of importance in the mathematics of earlier centuries provide clear evidence that it will continue to be of importance in the foreseeable future of mathematics. On the other hand, the role of the axiomatic method in high school mathematics is not as universally accepted, even though it has had a place in the teaching of school geometry throughout the history of western culture since the time of Eudoxus. In the last decade the relevance of the axiomatic method even to the teaching of high school geometry has been challenged in some quarters.

The point of view that I want to present here is to make a vigorous a defense as I can of the importance of teaching the axiomatic method in high school mathematics. I realize full well that it is not sufficient as an argument to point to the importance of the axiomatic method already in the teaching of university mathematics and in mathematical research.

There are three general arguments I would like to advance for emphasizing the axiomatic approach to mathematics in the high school curriculum. In the first place the axiomatic approach provides an important method of making the mathematics taught more elementary and the subject more restricted from the standpoint of what the student has to learn and encompass. An excellent example is provided by the real numbers. We now expect students to know a good deal about the real number system by the time they have finished high school mathematics, at least the students who are college bound and who take a full high school mathematics curriculum. If the properties of the real number system are taught from an axiomatic standpoint, the student is given a restricted list of properties that are fundamental and from which all others can be derived. Moreover, most of the axioms that are used express elementary properties that generalize in a natural way what the student has learned in earlier years. The axiomatic approach also assures the student that the properties he must know are restricted to those expressed by the axioms and the theorems that follow from the axioms. It is my own belief that it is all too easy for us confidently to assume that students are clear about the properties of the real numbers and have a good intuitive feeling for what the real numbers are.

This assumption, which I feel is unwarranted, is relatively crucial to those approaches to secondary school geometry that lean heavily on the properties of the real numbers.

Perhaps the best perspective in which to consider the axiomatic approach to the real number system is to ask what are the alternatives. It is doubtful that many people feel it would be wiser to go through the full mathematical construction of the real numbers via Dedekind cuts or Cauchy sequences of the rational numbers, and moreover it is doubtful that they would want to construct the rational numbers themselves as certain equivalence classes of ordered pairs of integers. An historically important alternative approach has been through the geometrical theory of real magnitudes, but it is doubtful that anyone will want the real numbers to be constructed out of geometrical entities. In any case, either of these prospective approaches is certainly less elementary than the axiomatic algebraic approach. I suppose that a fourth alternative is simply to leave the whole matter up in the air and to develop in a higgledy-piggledy fashion the properties needed, but I am skeptical that students will have the right sort of confidence and clarity about the properties of the real numbers when this approach is taken seriously.

My second argument centers around the importance of developing intuitions for finding and giving mathematical proofs. It is a common complaint about beginning graduate students in mathematics in the United States that one of their worst defects is their inability to write a coherent mathematical proof. A fortiori, this is even truer of undergraduate students of mathematics. And the reasons for this deficiency are not hard to find. Both at the school and university level explicit training in the writing of mathematical proofs and the explicit consideration of heuristic methods for finding proofs are woefully lacking in the curriculum. Systematic pursuit of the axiomatic method in high school mathematics provides perhaps the best opportunity for training students at an early stage in the finding and writing of mathematical proofs. It is all too easy to assume that as students develop an intuition for geometrical facts, for example, they will almost automatically be able to produce coherent proofs. Put another way, what I am saying is that I consider it just as necessary to train the intuition for finding and writing mathematical proofs as to teach intuitive knowledge of geometry or the real number system. I am contending that training in the finding and writing of proofs must be given as much explicit attention and should begin as early as other parts of the mathematical training of students; it is in the context of the elementary mathematics taught in high school that the student can first learn to work in a natural and easy way with axioms and the proofs of theorems that follow rigorously from the axioms.

My third argument for the use of the axiomatic method in high school mathematics centers around the increasing importance of learning how to think in a mathematical fashion as the total body of mathematics itself increases so rapidly. It is becoming clear that it is reasonably hopeless to expect students at any stage to master any substantial portion of extant mathematics. We can, of course, agree on the greater importance of certain parts of mathematics, but still a good case can be made that perhaps the best thing we can do for our students is to begin to teach them to think mathematically as effectively as possible. It has been my own experience that mathematicians discussing curriculum are uneasy in any attempt to characterize what they consider to be the essential nature of mathematical thinking. As mathematicians they are much more accustomed to thinking about mathematical objects and proving facts about these objects. In the same way, it is much easier to get a clear and sophisticated statement from a mathematician about why a given proof is correct or another proof contains an error than it is to get a subtle or relatively elaborate evaluation of the worth of one kind of heuristic reasoning versus another. Using an axiomatic approach in the teaching of mathematics provides a superb opportunity for more explicit emphasis on how proofs are found and what heuristic ideas are central to their discovery.

I would also like to urge the viewpoint that there is no fundamental conflict between the axiomatic method as pursued in pure mathematics and the development of skills for solving problems in applied mathematics. It has become all too fashionable at the present time to emphasize a conflict between pure and applied mathematics, and to be for the one and against the other in terms of what is to be emphasized in the mathematical training of students. From a psychological standpoint there is a very close affinity between the correct and complete statement of the mathematical conditions that characterize a problem in applied mathematics and the statement of axioms in pure mathematics. In both cases the aim is from a mathematical standpoint to make the problem at hand a tub on its own bottom, so to speak, without dependence in implicit and ill-understood ways on other parts of mathematics or on other physical side conditions. An experience that I would claim is psychologically identical to isolating the mathematical features of an applied problem is that of finding axioms for some part of pure mathematics. A weakness of our teaching of the axiomatic method is that we too seldom confront our students with the problem of formulating axioms, as opposed to deriving consequences from a clearly stated, teacher-provided set of axioms. In my own judgment, the present teaching of axiomatic mathematics at the school or university level is more deficient on this point than any other.

To give these general remarks a greater sense of definiteness, I now turn to some more constructive and particular ideas about the axiomatic method under the headings of logic, algebra, geometry and calculus.

71

Logic. As part of training in the axiomatic method in school mathematics, I would not advocate an excessive emphasis on logic as a self-contained discipline. For example, I do not really agree with those mathematicians who feel that logic should be studied in the form of Boolean algebra as an autonomous discipline early in the mathematical training of students. What I do feel is important is that students be taught in an explicit fashion classical rules of logical inference, learn how to use these rules in deriving theorems from given axioms, and come to feel as much at home with simple principles of inference like modus ponendo ponens as they do with elementary algorithms of arithmetic. I hasten to add that these classical and ubiquitous rules of inference need not be taught in symbolic form, nor do students need to be trained to write formal proofs in the sense of mathematical logic. What I have in mind is that the student should be able to recognize without second thought the correctness of the inference:

> If this figure is a square, then this figure is a quadrilateral.
> This figure is a square.
> Therefore, this figure is a quadrilateral.

And also to recognize the fallacious character of the inference:

> If this figure is a square, then this figure is a quadrilateral.
> This figure is a quadrilateral.
> Therefore, this figure is a square.   (Fallacious)

The classical forms of sentential inferences present no problem and are already covered in many of the modern textbooks on high school geometry. The real pedagogical problem centers around the making of valid inferences involving quantifiers. In this respect it seems to me that the best approach is the classical one of divide and conquer. What I mean by this is that students should first be introduced to substitution for individual variables where the only quantifiers implicitly understod are universal quantifiers standing at the beginning of a sentence and whose scopes are the remainder of the sentence. No other universal quantifiers and no existential quantifiers of any sort should be considered at this stage. For this restricted use of quantifiers, essentially only a simple rule of substitution of terms for variables and a correspondingly simple rule of generalization is required. In the paragraphs below I try to indicate how far this sort of logic can carry us in the elementary treatment of the algebra of real numbers and of vector geometry, without requiring the introduction of existential quantifiers and the subtle problems of inference that accompany these quantifiers. Only at a late stage in high-school mathematics would I recommend that inferences involving existential quantifiers be explicitly introduced, and then only sparingly.

72

The role I see for logic in teaching of the axiomatic methods in high school mathematics should be clear. Without training in the proving of theorems, the development of the axiomatic method is a sterile enterprise. It is important and essential that students learn how to make inferences from axioms in order to comprehend the power of the axiomatic method. To be able to make such inferences, they should be given training in the standard forms of inference that they may use in learning to think out and write down an acceptable mathematical proof. From years of grading mathematical proofs given on examinations at the university level, I am firmly convinced, as I have already indicated, that the ability to write a coherent mathematical proof does not develop naturally even at the most elementary levels and must be a subject of explicit training.

Algebra. The initial framework of logic described above, it is suggested, should be deliberately restricted to quantifier-free sentences in order to avoid the troublesome and subtle matter of handling existential quantifiers or universal quantifiers with restricted scope. The student is already familiar with this restricted logic, for it corresponds rather closely to the elementary arithmetic and algebra he has had prior to entering high school. The bulk of the algebra he has learned can now be codified in an elementary axiomatic fashion by deriving the consequences of the axioms for a Euclidean field, that is, an ordered field in which every nonnegative element is a square. We may avoid all existential quantifiers by replacing the three existential axioms:

$$(\forall x)\,(\exists y)\,(x + y = 0)$$
$$(\forall x)\,(\forall y)\,[if\, y \neq 0, then\, (\exists z)\,(x = y \cdot z)]$$
$$(\forall x)\,(if\, 0 < x, then\, (\exists y)\,(x = y \cdot y)$$

by the following three axioms which introduce the operations of subtraction, division and taking the square root of a positive number.

$$x - y = z\, if\, and\, only\, if\, x = y + z.$$
$$If\, y \neq 0, then\, x \div y = z\, if\, and\, only\, if\, x = y \cdot z.$$
$$If\, 0 < x, then\, \sqrt{x} = y\, if\, and\, only\, if\, x = y \cdot y\, and\, 0 < y.$$

In these terms then the elementary algebra taught in high school should mainly center around the consequences of the axioms that define a Euclidean field. In view of the three axioms just stated, which are introduced to eliminate existential quantifiers, the axioms as stated here for a Euclidean field use the operation symbols for addition, multiplication, subtraction, division, and taking the square root, the relation symbol "$<$" and the individual constants "0" and "1". The beauty of these axioms is that their intuitive content should be familiar to the students. Perhaps the only idiom that needs some explicit new discussion is the use of "if and only if" in the three axioms just mentioned. The full set of axioms is the following:

$$\text{(1)} \qquad x + y = y + x$$
$$\text{(2)} \qquad x \cdot y = y \cdot x$$
$$\text{(3)} \qquad (x + y) + z = x + (y + z)$$
$$\text{(4)} \qquad (x \cdot y) \cdot z = x \cdot (y \cdot z)$$
$$\text{(5)} \qquad x \cdot (y + z) = (x \cdot y) + (x \cdot z)$$
$$\text{(6)} \qquad x + 0 = x$$
$$\text{(7)} \qquad x \cdot 1 = x$$
$$\text{(8)} \qquad x - y = z \text{ if and only if } x = y + z.$$
$$\text{(9) If } y \neq 0, \text{ then } x \div y = z \text{ if and only if } x = y \cdot z.$$
$$\text{(10) If } x < y, \text{ then it is not the case that } y < x.$$
$$\text{(11) If } x < y \text{ and } y < z, \text{ then } x < z.$$
$$\text{(12) If } x \neq y, \text{ then } x < y \text{ or } y < x.$$
$$\text{(13) If } y < z, \text{ then } x + y < x + z.$$
$$\text{(14) If } 0 < x \text{ and } y < z, \text{ then } x \cdot y < x \cdot z.$$
$$\text{(15) If } 0 < x, \text{ then } \sqrt{x} = y \text{ if and only if } x = y \cdot y \text{ and } 0 < y.$$
$$\text{(16)} \qquad 0 \neq 1.$$

At a later stage and toward the end of high school mathematics for those who are taking a full program, it will be appropriate to go on to the concept of a real closed field, that is, a field that is Euclidean and is such that every polynomial of an odd degree with coefficients in the field has a zero in the field. (The choice of real closed fields as a terminal algebraic concept rests on the fact that every real closed field is elementarily equivalent with the field of real numbers; by this I mean that every first-order sentence which holds in one of these two fields holds in the other, and by "first-order" is meant sentences whose variables range only over elements of the field and not over sets of elements.)

Geometry. The appropriate axiomatic approach to elementary geometry is, as everyone knows, a much more controversial subject. If a vector-space approach is used, then it is possible to use the quantifier-free methods just described for algebra, and this has the important advantage of continuing to keep the structure of proofs simple. It also means that proofs can be a natural extension of the techniques already learned in algebra. Moreover, in line with the earlier remarks on algebra, I would propose vector spaces over Euclidean fields as the proper elementary objects of the theory. The axiomatic approach can take proper advantage of the fact that the vectors form a Abelian group under addition just as the real numbers or elements of a Euclidean field do, and therefore all elementary properties are shared. Elementary theorems about addition of vectors will have already been proved as elementary theorems about addition of numbers. To this vector-space structure may be added the concept of the inner product of two vectors to permit the introduction of concepts of distance and perpendicularity. The quantifier-free axioms on the inner product are just the following three, where α and β are real numbers, and x, y and z are vectors.

$$If\ x \neq 0,\ then\ x \cdot x > 0,$$
$$x \cdot y = y \cdot x,\ \text{and}$$
$$(\alpha x + \beta y) \cdot z = \alpha(x \cdot z) + \beta(y \cdot z).$$

Unfortunately for the treatment of many geometrical figures and their properties, which we expect our students to know, the purely vector-space approach does not provide a natural framework. For these developments, it is my own conviction that an intrinsic axiomatization that emphasizes the role of geometrical constructions is the most appealing. I realize however, that there is wide disagreement on this viewpoint. There are also pedagogical difficulties in providing a strictly axiomatic approach in terms of geometrical constructions. I will not pursue the point further here. It should be mentioned that still a third approach to elementary geometry is in terms of introducing geometrical transformations as well as vectors. It is thoroughly clear from recent discussions that it will be some time before the pedagogically most suitable set of axioms will be hit upon in terms of any of the approaches I have mentioned, but I would like to emphasize the importance of quantifier-free methods if we expect our students to become adept at finding and writing correct proofs. The logical complexities of most axiomatic approaches to geometry at the high school level make it difficult for students to acquire a clear and surefooted understanding of what mathematical arguments are all about.

Calculus. Space does not permit many comments on how the axiomatic approach may be applied to the teaching of calculus in high school, but the main thrust of what I want to say can be easily conjectured from what I have already said about algebra and geometry. An axiomatic approach in terms of "epsilon-delta" concepts and proofs does not seem appropriate. What does seem practical is an axiomatic algebraic approach to the calculus of elementary functions combined with considerable stress on the intuitive geometric and physical meaning of the derivative and integral of an elementary function. Moreover, the student can explicitly check the axioms by computing the areas of rectangles and triangles or the properties of rectilinear motion.

Again, I emphasize that a quantifier-free approach permits an easy but rigorous development of the elementary parts of the calculus, and the student can quickly be led to have a feel for the power of the calculus in solving empirically meaningful problems.*

* For those interested in quantifier-free arithmetic, an excellent survey is to be found in J. C. Shepherdson, "Non-standard models for fragments of number theory," *The Theory of Models*, edited by J. W. Addison, L. Henkin and A. Tarski, North-Holland Publishing Co., Amsterdam, 1965. One beautiful result is due to J. R. Shoenfield, "Open sentences and the induction axiom," *Journal of Symbolic Logic*, vol. 23 (1958), pp. 7–12. He proves that a system of nine axioms based on the successor ', predecessor P, and addition $+$ operations, and the constant 0, is not augmented in deductive power by the addition of the induction axiom for sentences without quantifiers. The nine axioms are just these.

(1) $\qquad x' \neq 0$
(2) $\qquad PO = 0$
(3) $\qquad Px' = x$
(4) $\qquad x + 0 = x$
(5) $\qquad x + y' = (x + y)'$
(6) $\qquad$ If $x \neq 0$, then $x = (Px)'$.
(7) $\qquad x + y = y + x$
(8) $\qquad (x + y) + z = x + (y + z)$
(9) $\qquad$ If $x + y = x + z$, then $y = z$.

■ *H. E. Vaughan*

A USE OF THE AXIOMATIC METHOD
IN TEACHING ALGEBRA

There is some disagreement as to the extent to which the axiomatic method is suitable for use in teaching high school mathematics. One opinion which is frequently expressed is that it is all right to use the axiomatic method in teaching high school geometry, but it is all wrong to use it in teaching high school algebra. It has been my experience that some of those who hold this opinion do so because, to them, the use made of the axiomatic method in algebra is of a different nature from its use in high school geometry. Once such a person is made aware of this and is shown that the axiomatic method can be used in teaching algebra in much the same way as it is used in teaching geometry, he is likely to express a different opinion. He may even go so far as to say that the use of the axiomatic method in teaching high school algebra is highly commendable.

In view of this, it seems to me that it may be worthwhile to point out some of the kinds of use which can, for various purposes, be made of the axiomatic method and then to indicate how the method can be used to advantage in teaching high school algebra.

According to the nature of one's current interests, he may view the axiomatic method as
   (1) a method of organizing part of his knowledge of some particular subject matter, or
   (2) a method for exploiting structural similarities among several subject matters, or
   (3) a method of characterizing a type of structure or an abstract deductive theory, or
   (4) a method for exploring a deductive theory—which theory may be either "concrete" or "abstract."

As illustrations of (1) one might cite J. H. Woodger's work on the foundations of genetics*, as well as the search for substitutes for Euclid's parallel postulate, prior to the discovery of non-Euclidean geometries.

---

*As reported, for instance, in *The Axiomatic Method*, edited by Henkin, Suppes and Tarski, North-Holland Publishing Co. 1959, pp 408–428.

As an illustration of (2) we may imagine an early stage in the development of group theory when it was realized that function composition imposes a "structure" on each set of permutations which is closed under composition and inversion; and that these structures are "similar" in certain interesting respects which can be specified by reference to properties of function composition. At a later stage it became profitable to define a group operation to be any function g such that

$$g(g(a,b),c) = g(a,g(b,c))$$

and there exist unique members x, y, and z of its domain such that

$$g(a,b) = x, g(a,y) = c, \text{and} g(z,b) = c$$

for any a, b, and c in its domain. This furnishes an illustration of (3).

Observation of the use made of such definitions probably had much to do with developing the notion of a deductive theory—a set of sentences (according to some well-defined sense of the word "sentence") which is deductively closed, that is, which contains each sentence which is deducible (again, according to well-defined rules) from any of its members. Such a deductive theory may be said to be concrete if its sentences are about some particular subject matter and to be abstract if its sentences contain completely undefined terms. From some points of view the distinction between concrete and abstract deductive theories is unimportant. After all, a concrete deductive theory can be turned into an abstract one merely by agreeing to forget the meanings of certain symbols; and an abstract deductive theory can be made concrete by assigning meanings to its undefined terms. For our purposes, however, the distinction will prove to be a vital one.

Finally—as to (4)—being given a deductive theory in some way, one may try to find comprehensible sets of its sentences from which the remaining sentences of the theory—or, at least, a respectable share of them—can be deduced. (This is somewhat analogous to the activity of a naturalist who attempts to learn about the life in a region by studying a collection of specimens of its animals and plants.) Such a search should yield information as to how the given theory hangs together and may, in expert hands, suggest other interesting and useful deductive theories.

Up to a few years ago, the only use made of the axiomatic method in high school was in the teaching of geometry. Here, in spite of anything the texts may have included concerning the undefined character of words such as "point" and "line", the viewpoint of the students and teachers was, for the most part, that described in (1). The axiomatic treatment of geometry in high school was—and, mostly, still is—a procedure for organizing some of one's beliefs concerning the geometry of physical space (and, of course, for attaining to new beliefs).*

After high school geometry, one's next opportunity to see the axiomatic method in action was in graduate or near-graduate college courses. Here, except in exceptional cases, the points of view were those described in (2), (3) and (4). In particular, in studying algebra one might, after an all too brief experience of (2), spend most of his time investigating well-defined but—in the classroom—infrequently exemplified types of structure. This could—and still can—be a somewhat frustrating experience for a student. Even those who were successful in making use of the axiomatic method from our viewpoints (3) and (4) were likely to become imbued with the feeling that "the" use of this method in the study of algebra requires, by the very nature of the subject matter, phenomenal powers of abstraction. The development of algebraic theory in recent years can well serve to strengthen such a feeling.

In view of all this—and the common frailty of human nature—it is not surprising that very competent and even eminent mathematicians should voice the opinion that, while it is all right to use the axiomatic method when teaching high school geometry, it is wrong to attempt to use it to teach algebra to high school students. When one means by this that, while a student will probably profit by the example of (1) which can be furnished by high school geometry, he will almost certainly be harmed if an attempt is made to require him to adopt (3) in his study of beginning algebra, I will heartily agree with him. High school is not the place to study the theory of complete ordered fields, the theory of ordered fields, or even, except in exceptional situations, to define the notion of a field. But it is an appropriate place to begin the axiomatic study of the real number system.

In spite of what has gone before, the assertions made at the end of the preceding paragraph may appear to contradict one another. After all, what is the difference between studying the theory of complete ordered fields and using the axiomatic method to study the algebra of the real numbers? In either case, one proceeds to investigate the consequences of the same set of axioms. Psychologically, the difference is a profound one. It is the difference between studying an abstract deductive theory and a concrete one— almost equivalently, it is the difference between adopting viewpoint (3) and adopting viewpoint (1). To do the former requires considerable "mathematical maturity"; the latter, as the history of teaching geometry might suggest, is within the capabilities of very many high school students.*

*What a text may say about undefined terms is very likely to be forgotten, by a student, under the impact of the pictures it offers in illustration of the occurrence of "angles", "arcs", and the like, in nature and in the works of man.
*See Appendix.

There remains the problem of how, exactly, the axiomatic method can be used in teaching high school algebra and the question as to whether, assuming that this can be done, it is worthwhile to do so. How one answers the question will depend, naturally, on how he solves the problem.

As to the problem, one may grant that, in applying the axiomatic method to geometry, a student feels—and legitimately so—that he is studying physical space of which he has some previous knowledge and that he is organizing his knowledge of it and gaining more. When it comes to algebra, however, a student rarely has any knowledge of the real numbers to begin organizing. This is surely not the time to introduce him to the real numbers, construed either as equivalence classes of Cauchy sequences of rational numbers or as Dedekind cuts. What is it that he is to gain knowledge of so that he can begin the job of organization and further learning?

To answer this question—or, more correctly, to assess its importance—it is useful to consider the corresponding question for geometry. A geometry student knows very well what geometry is about. His geometry is about physical space, and all his life has been spent in it. Nevertheless, if one were so ill-advised as to ask him what a point or a line is, he would be unlikely to come up with a satisfactory answer. His best response, probably, would be to say, "In geometry we don't define them; 'point' and 'line' are undefined terms." Of course, what he means is not that he is adopting viewpoint (3) but that, while he knows perfectly well what a point is, it's hard to put it into words—and, anyhow, it's an unfair question. Although some students may give lipservice to some vague notion of an "idealization" of physical space, their readiness to apply the axiomatic method to geometry is, in part, dependent on their willingness to subscribe to the fiction that, when doing so, they are, in fact, talking about physical objects. They are far from ready to adopt the view that they are developing an abstract deductive theory which, for rather obscure reasons, will help them to make approximately correct predictions concerning spacial relationships among physical objects.

We can now return to the question of how an eighth- or ninth-grade student can discuss real numbers and operations on them without knowing what they are. In the first place, he couldn't care less what they are. He has spent his life surrounded by things of various degrees of utility to him and it has probably never entered his mind to ask what they are—except in the sense of what words to use in speaking about them. More particularly, during all his school life he has been learning about various kinds of numbers and operations on them. If he could be brought to understand the question "What is the cardinal number 2?" he would be likely to consider it a dull one. He is satisfied with knowing what he can "do" with numbers, how he can "use" them. Because of past successes in this line (even partial ones), he is entirely ready to learn about real numbers without asking what they are. *But,* although he couldn't care less what they are, he assumes, without even thinking about it, that they are specific entities.

One way in which students can be made acquainted with the real numbers is by suggesting to them situations in which the "unsigned"—or nonpolar—numbers with which they are already acquainted prove inadequate. For example, although these nonpolar numbers are suitable as measures of trips taken along, say, an east-west road, they have no characteristic which can be correlated with the direction—easterly or westerly—of such a trip. More generally, although these numbers can be used very well as measures of quantity, they are not adequate in themselves when one wishes to measure changes—increases or decreases—in quantity. Faced with the problem of assigning measures to such changes, students are quite ready to believe that there are numbers which they can use for this purpose.* By suggesting problems concerning directed trips, it is easy to direct attention to an operation on the new numbers which, after a time, turns out to be sufficiently analogous to addition of the previously known numbers to warrant being also called "addition". By any one of many similar devices, students can be made aware of a second binary operation on the new numbers which, for similar reasons, it turns out to be reasonable to call "multiplication." The same devices which direct attention to these operations strongly suggest that each is associative and commutative and that the second is distributive with respect to the first. The same or other devices also suggest other operations and relations as well as numerous other "principles" concerning them. Students can now see that some of the principles they have discovered are consequences of others. About halfway through the course, they are ready to choose some of these principles as postulates and to begin a deductive organization of their new-found knowledge.* At this point, students of algebra are in a somewhat more comfortable position than are beginning geometry students. As has previously been argued, the latter must pretend to believe in a correspondence, which in fact does not exist, between the words they use and physical reality. The algebra students, on the other hand, are using a language which does serve to describe accurately the nonphysical reality which forms the subject matter they are investigating.

*When this approach is used, students can be led to suggest names for these new numbers. Even if the suggested numerals are not adopted for class use, the realization that notation is invented, and may be invented even by oneself, is a big step toward becoming a user—rather than an avoider —of mathematics.

* It will come to many readers as no surprise that the writer has been describing the approach to algebra developed by the University of Illinois Committee on School Mathematics (UICSM). See the text *High School Mathematics, Course 1*, by Beberman and Vaughan, published (1964) by D. C. Heath and Company.

Although there is now ample evidence that there is a way of using the axiomatic method in teaching high school algebra, there remains the question as to whether this is "a good thing" or "a bad thing." To begin with, let me say again that I heartily agree with those who believe that it would be an example of extreme pedagogical irresponsibility to present high school students with a set of sentences and say, "These are postulates for the real numbers. In this course we are going to learn about the real numbers by investigating the consequences of these postulates." This would indeed be a bad thing to do. It should be clear by now, however, that the course I am advocating—that of developing some acquaintance with the real number system as a unique entity and then using the axiomatic method to organize and extend the knowledge one has gained—is very different from this.*

Some of the advantages which the advocated procedure has over some others are not directly connected with the use of the axiomatic method. One of these should, however, be mentioned. This is that students come to have a sense of personal involvement in the development of the subject. This enhances, for them, the subject's value to a point where they are not inclined to ask, "What good is it?" Anyone who has done research can testify that something in which he has had a hand is, for that reason if for no other, important!

A more pertinent point is that, as it is used in such a course, the axiomatic method shows up as a powerful way of organizing knowledge. Students learn that one's choice of axioms is somewhat arbitrary—one man's axiom may be his neighbor's theorem. This emphasis on organization furnishes motivation for studying the process of deduction. If—as is sometimes asserted to be the case—the only function of deduction in mathematics were to certify results obtained by intuition, there would be little justification for using the axiomatic method at any level. In particular, students are usually convinced of the truth of a theorem before they attempt to derive it from axioms, and proof of it adds little or nothing to their belief in it. In this connection, there is a very relevant quotation from the Edinburgh mathematician John Playfair. In the preface to his *Elements of Geometry* he wrote, in 1795, the following:

*It is also significantly different from a popular procedure in which one "invents" negative numbers because it would be nice to be able to subtract, and defines multiplication in the so-extended system in such a way that it will have the pleasant property of being distributive with respect to addition. Although this procedure may be logically impeccable and, from a mathematician's viewpoint, well motivated, it is highly formal and very sophisticated. In the procedure described in the text, the real numbers—both positive and negative—are construed as relations among the nonpolar numbers. −2, for example, is the relation, among the nonpolar numbers, of being 2 less than. So, the real numbers are introduced specifically to serve the purpose for which they are commonly used—that of measuring increases and decreases in quantities whose amounts are measured by nonpolar numbers.

It has been objected to many of the writers in Elementary Geometry, and particularly to Euclid, that they have been at great pains to prove the truth of many simple propositions, which everybody is ready to admit, without any demonstration, and thus take up the time, and fatigue the attention of the student, to no purpose. . . . Indeed, those who make the objection just stated, do not seem to have reflected sufficiently on the end of Mathematical Demonstration, which is not only to prove the truth of a certain proposition, but to shew its necessary connection with other propositions and its dependence on them. The truths of Geometry are all necessarily connected with one another, and the system of such truths can never be rightly explained, unless that connection be accurately traced, wherever it exists. It is upon this that the beauty and peculiar excellence of the mathematical sciences depend. . . .

To all this it may be added, that the mind, especially when beginning to study the art of reasoning, cannot be employed to greater advantage than in analyzing those judgements, which, though they appear simple, are in reality complex. . . .

Students who have used the axiomatic method to organize their recently acquired knowledge of the real numbers, and to obtain new results, see the advantages of applying the same method when they come to study geometry. They are not inclined to complain, "Why should I have to prove this? Anybody knows it's true." In addition to this attitude, the experience gained in proving theorems about real numbers prepares students to tackle the more complex proofs of geometric theorems. It could well be argued that, due to the complexity of its structure, Euclidean geometry is the subject least suited for one's initiation to the use of the axiomatic method or to the process of deduction. Fortunately, the theory of real numbers is admirably suited to these ends.

If, as I believe is the case, much of the value of the study of mathematics lies in the resulting development of a student's power to think clearly and to organize his knowledge, it seems obvious that such a use of the axiomatic method in the teaching of high school algebra as has been outlined is a very good thing.

Finally—in answer to an objection which is sometimes voiced—just as a deductive treatment of geometry does not hinder a student in learning to solve geometric problems, neither does a deductive approach to algebra make it more difficult for him to develop manipulative skills and to use algebra in solving problems. In either case—geometry or algebra—his development of the deductive theory should give him practice in the requisite skills and confidence in his ability to apply them to new problems. On the other hand, although his experience with the two deductive theories should give him a firm basis from which to proceed in applying his knowledge of geometry and algebra to the solution of problems, it is not to be expected that it, alone, will turn him into an efficient user of mathematics. His courses must be more than examples of the axiomatic method. The latter is not a cure-all for pedagogical ills, but—properly used—it is a powerful aid in learning and in gaining confidence in one's ability to make use of his knowledge.

APPENDIX

I realize that there is still a possibility that some readers will not be ready to grant that there is a difference between studying the theory of complete ordered fields and studying the real number system axiomatically. It is not unknown for a mathematician to tell his students that when he says "the real numbers" he is referring to any complete ordered field. After all (he may say), since any two such fields are isomorphic, any two are really the same one—they differ in name only. So, why give them different names? This attitude seems to me like that of a man whose current interest in human beings is restricted to their sex and who, as a consequence insists on calling every man "George" and every woman "Doll". After all (he might say), any two men, or women, are really the same—they differ in name only. Isn't it silly of you to call them by different names?

The moral of this is that, while anyone is entitled to refer to any chosen complete ordered field as "the real number system"—and, upon due notice, to change his choice as to which field he distinguishes in this way—a minimal respect for the use of language in communication should restrain him to employ a definite description (roughly, a the-phrase) to refer, on any one occasion, to a definite object.

■ *Gail S. Young*

THE ROLE OF POSTULATES
IN SCHOOL MATHEMATICS

To explain my view of the use of axioms in school mathematics, I would like to begin by discussing the role of the axiomatic method in contemporary mathematics. I can do no better than to quote five distinguished American mathematicians, A. Adrian Albert, Felix E. Browder, I. N. Herstein, Irving Kaplansky, and Saunders Mac Lane:[1]

> "Mathematics is the science of structure. Where intuition and unanalyzed experience indicate the existence of common structural features in a number of varying contexts, it is the task of mathematics to formulate these basic structural features in a precise and objective form. The mathematician *abstracts* from other variant and irrelevant features of these contexts in order to focus on these basic relations, and then must ask (and find out) what consequences follow from the basic relations alone. In its baldest form, this is the so-called axiomatic method, and one must always remark that the justification of a system of axioms lies in what can be proved from them, in what insights of a significant kind they furnish about the context from which the axioms sprang. . . . Once crystallized in a definite form and proved fruitful, the acts and processes and objective difficulties of a mathematical theory may provide the context for the creation of a new mathematical theory on a higher level by a new act of mathematical abstraction. Yet this new abstraction is justified not by any passion for abstraction for its own sake but by the urgent pressures of mathematical discovery, whose process is not an idle weaving of fantasies without limitation but rather a confrontation with the implacable enemy of the unknown, unstructured, and inaccessible."

To this I would like to add two comments. The first is that I believe people not themselves engaged in research do not appreciate that mathematics as defined above is in many ways an experimental discipline. In attempting to decide what properties are the important ones to build an abstraction on, or in attempting to discover the appropriate theorems, mathematicians look at many concrete situations, each corresponding to a laboratory experiment in the empirical sciences. If not quite concrete, the situations are at least at a lower level of abstraction.

For the second, notice that nothing whatever was said in this statement about rigor. One certainly wants rigorous proofs; but that is not the point of

[1]Letter, *Science*, 16 July 1965, Vol. 149, pp. 243–244.

the postulational method. It is to formulate and study "basic structural features in a precise and objective form."

In this task, there is great need for rigor, and it must be learned. But the reason is that, with a brain presumably designed by evolution to outwit saber-toothed tigers, we must somehow understand abstractions from abstractions from abstractions, and the best mathematicians still make mistakes. Learning how to be rigorous is a difficult, exacting task. In fact, I believe a main goal of Ph.D. training is to teach the student how to tell whether his argument is a correct proof or not.

If we are to be rigorous, we must have somewhere a set of statements that we use as ultimate reasons. Otherwise we get infinite arguments or circular ones. That is, rigorous arguments are necessarily postulational. In the traditional undergraduate curriculum, it is easy to overlook this. I do not know, for example, of a textbook in differential equations that is rigorous in the sense that it contains a complete, self-contained body of statements from which all the other statements in the book follow. I do not propose that someone write such a book. But it would be easy in such a course to forget the structure underlying it.

It is still possible to continue in the spirit of this old undergraduate curriculum, do graduate work, do socially valuable research, and never come to terms with contemporary mathematics or really master the sort of rigor needed for structural argument. It is certainly possible for the secondary school teacher to be in this position. Indeed, before the work of such groups as the Committee on the Undergraduate Program in Mathematics' Teacher Training Panel or before the National Science Foundation Institute program, few secondary teachers in this country were in any other position. It is natural that many teachers found in their retraining the idea of rigorous mathematics to be very difficult and did not master it in the couple of summers they spent in study. Not surprisingly, some of these overemphasize rigor in their own teaching. Exactly the same thing can be said of some college teachers or textbook writers. This has been responsible, I believe, for many distortions in school mathematics. When I see a seventh-grade text (age 12–13) that treats rational numbers as equivalence classes of ordered pairs of integers, and another that defines them as formal solutions of equivalence classes of equations $mx = n, m$ and n integers, I can only account for the books by such an explanation.

One can make a useful distinction between a rigorous proof and a convincing argument. There are many results in mathematics that one can (more or less) understand without a proof, for example, that a continuous function that is positive at one point and negative at another must be zero somewhere between. No student has difficulty in understanding this theorem or in believing it the first time it is used. In fact, it is quite difficult to get him to see any necessity for supplying a proof. There are other results that require an argument before they are understood. Take the theorem that the sum of the first n odd numbers is n^2. One can give a rigorous proof of this result by mathematical induction. But although this convinces a student that the result is safe to use, still he does not feel he understands it. The convincing argument is to put down one dot, then put down three dots to form a 2×2 square, then five dots to form a 3×3 square, then seven dots, ... This is vastly more informative than the argument by induction. (Unless one has started one's course with the Peano postulates for the whole numbers, the first argument is not really rigorous; of course, the second argument can be made just as rigorous. If you try this you will find an induction somewhere.)

The point that I have tried to make in these last few paragraphs is that the real spirit of contemporary mathematics is that of creative understanding, of abstraction for greater clarity of thought and ease of proof, of experimental study of the relatively concrete. It is not rigorous deduction of theorems from fixed postulate sets. That is a tool, not the goal. If you are to be an artist, you must learn how to mix colors well. But art is not the mixing of colors; it is the painting of pictures, and the training of the young artist should include the painting of as good pictures as he is technically capable of, while improving his technical skills.

Let me turn from these general considerations to school mathematics. I will speak only of the curriculum for those students planning further education, those that we call in the United States the "college-bound." It has been traditional in all countries that these students are prepared for calculus, whether as a last course in the secondary school, or a first course in college, and I do not see any great change occurring in this. It is, however, true that other types of mathematics are increasing in importance at the early stages of a college education. I mention linear algebra, probability, group theory for physical chemistry, game theory, computer science, as courses now needed by many students in the first two years of college. The schools must prepare many more students for many more types of mathematical experience.

The school program should come closer to presenting mathematics as it really is than it has done in the past. How is it to do this?

One proposal could be to begin the study of algebra with some simple set of axioms, say those for a group. One could state and prove a sequence of theorems and require the students to learn the proofs and to make simple ones for themselves. What is wrong with this is that it puts all the emphasis on rigorous proof. The student sees no differences between one theorem and another, except in the difficulty of the proof, and indeed he cannot, because he knows very little about the structures that are being abstracted. Re-

87

member "the justification of a system of axioms lies . . . in what insights of a significant kind they furnish about the context from which the axioms sprang." If, for the student, there are few such contexts, there are few insights. He is not studying structure, he is studying rigorous proofs.

It would be possible to take a great deal of time, say a year, and give a rich experience in group theory by studying many concrete groups and seeing how the group axioms explain their structures, that is, by carrying out many experiments. I am far from saying that this should not be done. I would have many questions: Can it be taught? What must be left out to give the necessary time? What changes are produced in the students? But thought and experiment can answer these. What I am saying is that to stop far short of such a treatment of group theory is to reduce the study of the group axioms to a sterile exercise in rigor.

The technical difficulty is that the group axioms are not categorical, are very far from categorical. That is, there are many essentially different systems satisfying the axioms, and the student has familiarity with almost none of them. What structures the student does have experience with are the ring of integers, the rational field, the real field, and possibly the complex field. These are also the objects that he must master for his most pressing task, the calculus.

Should the student study the integers as an axiomatic system, perhaps starting with the Peano axioms? I do not believe he should. The integers are too close to us for it to seem to the student anything but the most formal manipulation to prove from axioms that multiplication of integers is commutative. What are important are such things as the principle of mathematical induction and the unique factorization theorem. The second can be proved from the first, but it is much more important to understand them than to see this proof. At this level, there are more mathematics in a proof, even though not axiomatic, that there are an infinity of primes than in pages of arguments axiomatically justifying common arithmetic.

The real numbers are different. Here is a rich system with a simply stated categorical set of axioms, the axioms for a complete ordered field. Its most interesting properties are not known to the student and can be gradually unfolded throughout several years, by a systematic introduction of a more and more abstract approach. With commutativity, distributivity, etc., explicitly taught in the elementary school, as is becoming common here, the introduction of these field properties in the first algebra course and the use of them in studying the classical manipulations of elementary algebra can be done naturally. The point of view should be that the axioms are simply properties of the real numbers that we are using as a firm base for study. Pedagogical considerations may lead a teacher to introduce such a thing as a field of residues modulo some prime, but the motive should be to make clearer the reason for care, rather than the intrinsic interest of such a field.

In other words, I believe that the postulational study of algebra in the secondary school should be rather informal and aimed at an understanding of the real numbers and calculations with them preparatory to calculus. A postulational approach to algebra is not satisfactory because the proofs are too simple in nature to give any real idea about the nature of mathematical invention, because the theorems are (usually) only facts about numbers that the student has learned in arithmetic, and because he has no background of examples to justify the care required.

The course that has the strongest tradition of axiomatics is geometry. Geometry in the secondary school seems to me to be the material most like contemporary mathematics in its nature. There is a rich body of theorems with proofs that require real insight to formulate. What student expects, for example, that an angle inscribed in a semicircle is a right angle, and how many of them see at once why it is so? The arguments are logically more complicated, and verbal precision is required. There are also many results that a student can prove himself and get some feel of creative work.

What postulate sets are suitable? Euclid's, or the school revisions of Euclid's, are no longer satisfactory. It is not so much the omission of vital assumptions that is objectionable, to my mind, as the imprecision of concept and language. But there are many alternatives, such as the Birkhoff-Beatley axioms in terms of ruler and protractor that have been used in several textbooks in this country, or the European axioms in terms of rigid motions which are perhaps even more in the spirit of modern mathematics.

Better than geometry for an experience with postulational work is the elementary topology of the real line, which in a sense is the source of the contemporary approach to mathematics. But it would be hard for me to say that at the secondary level that material is of such importance for college-bound students that they should cover it.

There is a movement to cut down sharply on axiomatic geometry in the schools, to perhaps 10 or 12 propositions, in favor of an increase in analytic geometry. The case is utilitarian, I understand, for better preparation for calculus. However, it seems to me to be a loss of intellectual content, and of mathematics. The pressure for more mathematics in the same time is certainly great. But "more mathematics" should mean more real mathematical power, more familiarity with logic and structure, more hard problems solved, rather than more facts learned and techniques mastered.

I expect two groups to disagree with what I have written. One group would like much more postulational work, much more "pure mathematics", in the schools than I would. I would ask them to say how, short of very drastic changes, they can get enough examples of the systems being abstracted to make it meaningful. I would also ask them what would happen to the great majority of students who will use more mathematics later, but for whom this will mean calculus.

The other group is the group of users of mathematics—the engineer, physicist, etc. To them, I would point out, first, that I have not talked about all of school mathematics, merely of one aspect, the role of postulates. I believe students should be better prepared for calculus than ever before, and I believe that one way to get better preparation is to get better conceptual understanding. But that statement is still something of an evasion. The fact is that our view of mathematics has been revolutionized in the past 30 years. On the one hand, pure mathematics has been unified in a way that was thought to be lost forever, by such concepts as category and functor. The unification will have important consequences for the most concrete user of mathematics, and we are training for the future. On the other hand, the computer abolishes part of the need for technique, and raises the rest to a level of requiring conceptual understanding. One must try to get something of the spirit of modern mathematics over to our 15-year-olds, because when they are 45, that is part of what they will have to understand as physicists, engineers, etc.

■ *R. P. Dilworth*

THE ROLE OF PROBLEMS
IN MATHEMATICAL EDUCATION

Introduction

During the past decade, there has been a large and sustained effort directed toward curriculum reform in elementary and secondary mathematics. In the United States, this curriculum reform movement has been accompanied by a variety of experimental programs concerned with the development of new methods of teaching mathematics. In particular, special emphasis has been devoted to the use of "discovery" teaching methods in the mathematics classroom. Underlying both the curriculum development efforts and the teaching experimentation has been the realization that mathematics is not something which is passively learned, but is something which people do. Specifically, mathematics, at all levels, is chiefly concerned with problem solving in its most general sense. Accordingly, it is not surprising that there has been a growing awareness of the importance of problems both in textual material and in classroom instruction. Thus, in the report of the Cambridge Conference on School Mathematics[1] it is stated that "the construction of problem sequences is one of the largest and most urgent tasks in curriculum development."

Traditional mathematics texts have nearly always included extensive collections of exercises and problems. For the most part, these problems were designed to illustrate the text material and to give the student an opportunity to practice the related mathematical skills. The construction of problem sets to achieve such objectives is reasonably straightforward, even though it may require considerable effort and experience to develop carefully graded sequences of well formulated problems of this type. On the other hand, the experimental curricula and teaching methods which are now being developed aim at broader and deeper objectives. Instead of concentrating on formal skills, they strive for a higher level of mathematical understanding and seek to stimulate creative and independent thinking. Clearly, the most carefully constructed sequences of problems of traditional type are not appropriate for the new curriculum material. Furthermore, the most elegant and insightful presentation of mathematical text material is very likely to be ineffective if the associated problem sets are routine and uninspired. For it is in problem solving activities that the students acquire a working knowledge of the ideas

---

[1] "Goals for School Mathematics," Educational Services, Inc., Boston, Mass., Houghton Mifflin Co., 1963.

91

which are presented in the text and in the classroom. Thus problem sets must be developed which will effectively implement the objectives of the new curricula. The construction of such problems is a much more difficult task than that of preparing problems the principal aim of which is the development of formal skills. Nevertheless, as far as the development of effective curriculum material is concerned, this task is of fundamental importance and it must be undertaken with vigor and imagination.

In the following paragraphs, I intend to give some indication of the kinds of problem development which will be needed and to suggest some ways in which these tasks may be approached.

Problem Solving Objectives

It has already been observed that the principal objectives of the new mathematics curricula are to give students deeper understanding of the basic mathematical concepts and to stimulate them to do creative and independent thinking with these concepts. Accordingly, it must be the general purpose of the problem sets to implement these objectives. But such broad objectives are difficult to achieve directly and hence they should be described in terms of suitable intermediate objectives.

First of all, it should be observed that the development of formal skills is included in the general objectives, since these formal skills are part of the tools which are used in creative mathematical activity. Hence problem sets should provide adequate experience for the development of formal skills. However, if this is all that a problem set accomplishes, it will have failed to achieve its main purpose. Ideally, the experience with formal skills should occur naturally, but incidentally, in solving problems which are primarily designed to broaden understanding and to stimulate creative thinking.

While it is easy to state that problems should be designed to broaden mathematical understanding, it is very difficult to describe precisely how this may be achieved. Mathematical understanding is a complicated cognitive process and attempts to break it down into well-defined, independent components have not been highly successful. Nevertheless, when a specific problem is under consideration, there is usually general agreement on whether or not it contributes significantly to mathematical understanding. This suggests that, instead of describing objectives in terms of specific cognitive variables, it may be more useful to fix attention upon a particular mathematical concept and then analyze the ways in which problems can contribute to the understanding of the concept. In detail, the results of such an analysis will depend upon the particular concept under consideration. Nevertheless, there are some aspects of such an analysis which apply quite generally and which afford useful intermediate objectives for problem construction. It may be helpful to formulate a few of these principles explicitly.

(1) *Formulate problems in such a way that understanding of the particular concept is essential to the solution.*

As a very simple example, consider the concept of division of integers. A typical problem might be the following: Divide 108 by 9. Presented in this form the solution requires only elementary formal skill in division. On the other hand, the same problem can be stated as follows: Find the number which when multiplied by 9 yields 108. In this form, the solution requires an understanding of the basic relationship between multiplication and division.

This principle of problem formulation is not difficult to apply and yet it is often neglected in practice. In many cases, its use can convert routine drill exercises into problems with challenge and interest.

(2) *Formulate problems in such a way that there is a particularly elegant and efficient solution if the mathematical concept involved is properly understood.*

Problems formulated in this manner reward mathematical understanding in an immediate and practical way; namely, the problem solver finds a quick and aesthetically pleasing solution. In addition he may experience something of the feeling of elation which comes to the puzzle solver when he discovers the key to the puzzle. As a simple illustration consider the following problem: Calculate $24 \times 37 + 24 \times 63$. If it is recognized that the distributive law can be applied, then the solution involves at most trivial mental arithmetic. On the other hand, failure to use distributivity leads to extensive arithmetical computations.

(3) *Formulate problems in such a way that the mathematical principle must be applied in an unfamiliar setting.*

Nearly every mathematical concept can be applied in many different ways and in a variety of circumstances. Thus the ability to recognize and apply the principle in a very few situations can hardly be called true mathematical understanding. Accordingly it is important that the problems should be constructed which cover as wide a variety as possible of the ways in which the principle can be used. For example, for students who are familiar with elementary trigonometry, the equation $\cos 2x + 2 \cos x = \frac{1}{2}$ provides an application of the solution of quadratic equations in a setting quite different from the usual one.

(4) *Formulate problems in such a way that the solution requires a slightly extended or altered form of the mathematical concept.*

An important part of mathematical understanding is the recognition of possible extensions or modifications of particular mathematical principles. In fact, understanding of this kind is a necessary prerequisite for creative mathematical thinking. For example, the mathematical ideas associated with the solution of ordinary arithmetical problems need modification when the ordinary arithmetic is replaced by modular arithmetic.

(5) *Formulate problems in such a way that the mathematical principle appears to apply although the solution must actually be obtained in some other way.*

An important part of understanding a mathematical principle is the ability to recognize when it does not apply as well as when it does. Skillfully designed problems which tempt the solver to use a principle either incorrectly or unproductively can be very effective in sharpening a student's understanding of a mathematical concept. A typical illustration is the following: Find n such that $(37 - 18) - 11 = 37 - (n - 11)$. In this case, the use of associativity, which is highly tempting, is incorrect.

In addition to contributing to mathematical understanding, problem sets should also stimulate creative and independent thinking. Indeed, problems play a crucial role in this aspect, since the passive acquisition of knowledge from a text is certainly not creative thinking. In order to be creative the student must either pose problems for himself, or stimulating problems and questions must be presented to him. Now, if it is hard to determine the cognitive components of mathematical understanding, it is much more difficult to describe the components of creative mathematical thinking. In fact, most discussions of creativity in mathematics resort finally to the consideration of specific examples. For it is much easier to get agreement on whether or not a given piece of mathematics represents creative work than it is to agree on what characteristics of the work make it creative. Nevertheless, in order to understand the role of problems in promoting creativity, it will hardly suffice to merely consider examples. For some guiding principles are needed if ideas for problems are to be developed which are quite different from those which are already known. Furthermore the formulation of such principles requires an understanding of at least some aspects of the creative process.

Now a key feature of most mathematical thinking is the recognition of certain significant similarities common to some conceptual patterns. This feature is clearly evident in the solution of routine arithmetical problems where an algorithm already carried out on one set of numbers is applied to a new set. But it is also characteristic of some of the most abstract and recondite mathematics. It may well be that with a sufficiently broad interpretation of "similarities" and "patterns" all mathematical reasoning could be subsumed in this type of activity. The criteria for significance will depend upon the particular context. In some cases, this criterion may be usefulness in application or contribution to a solution of an important problem. In other cases, it may be simply the intrinsic difficulty involved in recognizing the similarity. But in any case, a principal cognitive feature of mathematical activity is the recognition of a significant sequence of similarities common to a set of conceptual patterns.

It is clear that the recognition of an obvious similarity common to a set of patterns is in no sense creative thinking. In fact, drill problems whether in arithmetic or in the calculus are precisely of this character. It should be mentioned, however, that some of the most creative perceptions in mathematics were perfectly obvious once they had been pointed out. One aspect, then, of creative thinking is the ability to recognize nonobvious and subtle similarities.

Mathematical activity rarely consists of the recognition of a single similarity, but usually involves a sequence of such recognitions, some of which depend upon previous ones. The process of carrying out the steps of a prescribed algorithm is an example of such a sequence of similarity recognitions. Also, it is in no sense creative mathematical work. Thus, if a sequence of similarity perceptions is to be creative it should exhibit some nonobvious and hence insightful features. Some of the perceptions themselves may be insightful. In other cases, the individual perceptions may be obvious, but the sequence as a whole may be quite nonobvious. Indeed, there have been sequences of almost trivial mathematical observations which have lead to very profound conclusions.

In the previous paragraph it was emphasized that mathematical activity usually consists of a sequence of perceptions. Some similarity recognitions lead naturally to others and may, in fact, generate many sequences of significant perceptions. Others, even though they are difficult and subtle, may be unproductive in developing new lines of mathematical thought. In some cases, the recognition of a possible line of development from a particular perception or observation may itself require a great deal of insight. At any rate, it is clear that another important aspect of creative thinking is the ability to recognize relationships which have a potential for generating others and then to use these relationships to develop new ones to stimulate creative thinking.

In terms of the construction of problems, these considerations suggest that *problems should be formulated which present the student with an opportunity to perceive significant mathematical relationships capable of leading to a variety of significant nonobvious conclusions.* Such problems are not likely to be individual exercises, but will consist of questions which define problem areas. It will be characteristic of the problem area that answers to the basic questions lead to new questions of interest.

As an example of a problem area which affords a variety of opportunities for creative thinking, consider the following construction: Begin with a sequence of, say, five boxes.

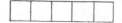

Write two numbers, say 2 and 3, in the first two boxes and then fill the remaining boxes in sequence by writing in the sum of the numbers in the previous two boxes. This gives the following configuration:

| 2 | 3 | 5 | 8 | 13 |

Thus far the construction involves only elementary arithmetic. But consider the following question: If the first and last numbers in the sequence are given, how can the second number be determined? Thus a configuration like the following is given:

| 11 | | | 43 |

The problem is to fill in the missing numbers. This is clearly much harder than the problem of filling in the numbers when the first two numbers are given.

If there are only three boxes, a very little insight shows that the missing number is obtained by subtracting the first number from the last. This solution may suggest some conjectures for the case of four boxes. On the other hand, it may be necessary to do some experimentation. When the solution for four boxes is obtained, still further experimentation and hypothesis making may be necessary for the case of five boxes. Throughout the analysis there are many opportunities to compare patterns and observe significant similarities. Even after a general solution has been found, there are many further questions which naturally arise. For example, how can other numbers in the sequence be determined directly? What happens if the rule for generating the sequence is changed? What if other configurations of boxes are used? These questions can lead to many different lines of creative thought.

Mathematical games, in addition to being an interesting classroom activity, frequently afford opportunities for creative thinking. As an illustration, consider the class of Nim-type games. Perhaps the simplest example is the following: Two persons play the game. The first player chooses one of the numbers 1 or 2. The second player likewise chooses one of the numbers 1 or 2 and adds it to the number chosen by the first player. The players continue to play alternately, each time choosing one of the numbers 1 or 2 and adding to the sum already obtained. The first player to make the sum equal to 10 wins. The basic question is the following: What is the best choice in the first play? Children playing this game may discover the answer by experience. But the answer can also be obtained by some elementary but insightful analysis. The key step in discovering the answer is realizing that one must first consider the end of the game. The next step is recognizing that if one reaches 7 in the play, then one can always win regardless of the opponent's play. But then it is an easy step to see that if one reaches 4, then one can always reach 7 and hence win. The final step is to observe that the best first choice is the number 1, since then one can always reach 4, 7, and 10 in that order and hence win. A student who makes such an analysis has clearly done some creative thinking. But then he can proceed to formulate and study many further questions. What happens if the target number is changed? What if the set of choice numbers is made quite arbitrary? What if the single target number is replaced by a set of numbers? What happens if the single sum is replaced by two or more sums so that the players may choose which sum they wish to increase?

96

It is clear that there is an unlimited number of modifications and generalizations which lead to interesting mathematical questions.

The previous examples were arithmetical in nature. The final example is a geometrical problem which likewise affords many opportunities for creative thinking. The problem is the following: What is the largest number of regions which can be formed by six lines in the plane? Again it is helpful to begin with a small number of lines and try to generalize. The ability to recognize significant patterns is highly important in reaching a solution. Having obtained the solution for six lines, one can ask for the solution for n lines where n is quite arbitrary. Other significant questions can be asked. What happens if lines are replaced by another class of curves in the plane? What is the answer to the corresponding question concerning planes in space?

Problem Set Development

In textbook writing the author usually concentrates on the organization and presentation of the expository material. The preparation of problem sets is frequently a necessary but unattractive chore. Thus it is hardly surprising that interesting and imaginative problem sets are rarely developed. Furthermore, even if the author had the necessary interest in producing challenging problem sets, it is not likely that he would have the skill and insight required to devise such problems. For the design of problems of the type contemplated in this article is not unlike a mathematical research project. The same kind of originality in the generation of ideas is required. In some respects, it presents more of a challenge than mathematical research, since the ideas must be formulated within the framework of the concepts and techniques of elementary and secondary mathematics.

Problem set development should not be a sideline activity of the textbook writer. It should rather be a principal effort of the curriculum development program. Furthermore, this task deserves the attention of the most original minds in the mathematical community. It may even be appropriate to organize extensive problem set development projects just as research projects are now organized. The goal of this effort would be the construction of a body of problem material which would provide the environment for imaginative and creative thinking at every point in the mathematics curriculum.

■ *N. J. Fine*

SOME THOUGHTS ON PROBLEM SOLVING

Anyone who has worked with young children knows how readily they respond to number games and puzzles. How does it happen, then, that after a few years of schooling many of them have acquired negative attitudes towards mathematics? It is all too easy to blame their teachers, but they also are products of the same stultifying process.

One possible place to break the vicious cycle is at the teacher-training level. Perhaps, in addition to the serious courses we prescribe for them, we should have them participate in a class devoted to the fun and enjoyment of mathematics. There are many books on recreational mathematics from which to select suitable problems. Each of us has a few favorite chestnuts, which could be shared and collected. Such a collection could be dipped into from time to time in order to brighten the arithmetic period. Perhaps a daily teaser could be presented.

Do our prospective teachers have time in their programs for such a course? I suggest that we should make the time, either as part of a methods course or in place of one.

A problem-solving course of this type need not be mere frills and furbelows to decorate the austere shape of "serious" mathematics. Properly presented, it could go to the heart of mathematical pedagogy. Indeed, it is difficult to imagine what the teaching of mathematics would be like without problems. Student activity is the most important ingredient of the learning process, and problem solving is the most common and effective form of activity. Student attitudes are strongly conditioned by the types of problems proposed, especially in the early grades. If these attitudes are not as favorable as we would like them to be, we would do well to examine carefully the tasks we set for our students.

A reappraisal of subject matter is also in order, but it is folly to hope that "new mathematics" taught in dull routine fashion will work a miraculous cure. It is good to discard prejudices about the kinds of mathematics children are ready for or capable of at various ages. It is good to experiment with the introduction of sets, logic, geometry, matrices, number theory, and so on, in the early grades. These subjects can be a rich source of problem material, but their intrinsic interest can all too easily be dissipated by repetitious and purposeless problems.

What makes a good problem? The most crucial requirement is that the student want to solve it. Of course initially he may just wish to please the teacher or earn a good grade, but such motivations do not last long unless supplemented by a challenge in the problem itself. If he is acquiring a skill, the challenge may simply be "Can I do it?" Once he feels that that challenge is met, further drill is likely to be resented, even though it may be necessary for mastery. The exercise of the skill must then become a means to some other desirable end. For example, he can get plenty of practice in addition while checking or discovering regularities in the Fibonacci sequence ($F_0 = 0, F_1 = 1$, $F_{n+2} = F_{n+1} + F_n$). Finding square roots by iteration can provide motivated practice in division. A single 2×2 matrix multiplication contains 8 multiplications and 4 additions—a very respectable brushup.

Of course a problem should be "meaningful" to the student, but we can err in two directions in interpreting that adjective. First, telling some trumped-up story about Farmer Brown and his crops or about the brave little newsboy with a sliding scale of prices for his papers may strike very few responsive chords in our students. Even our heroic astronauts may fail to spark their interest if the problems solved in their names are intrinsically uninteresting. Second, we may be missing golden opportunities by avoiding number puzzles or experiments with numbers for fear that they are not concrete enough. If psychologists have not discovered a "puzzling instinct" in man, it is only because they haven't looked, for I am sure that it's there. The strong appeal of games such as chess, checkers, or cards shows that connections with "real life" or the student's "experience" are not necessary for an activity to be meaningful. The world of "mods" can be fascinating to a seven-year-old, and needs no more introduction than "Let's pretend that 5 is the same as 0. Then what is 6?" The discovery of the periodic pattern formed by the Fibonacci numbers mod m can be a very satisfying and instructive experience for him. To search for and perceive pattern is a genuine mathematical activity and it is never too early to begin it. Number theory is an excellent source of problems at all levels. (How do the 2-table and the 3-table intersect? What about the 4-table and the 6-table?) So are experiments with probability and statistics. (Try the problème des rencontres with 10 cards). A great deal of intuitive geometry can be developed by means of problems. Indeed, it is interesting to conjecture how much systematic teaching could be done through problems alone.

It is an excellent idea for a problem to foreshadow future developments, to teach as well as test. For example, in analytic geometry the calculation of slopes between successively closer points on a curve can start a student thinking about tangents and derivatives before he has even heard the terms. Trying to solve $ax \equiv 1 \pmod{m}$ for various values of a and m can impress on him the difference between a ring and a field before he knows what either one is. He can get used to making functional tables long before the formal introduction of the function concept.

There is another place where a problem solving course or seminar might be very effective. That is at the senior level for mathematics majors in college. Here it would serve the purpose of integrating the student's knowledge and introducing him to research. The emphasis might be on his asking fruitful questions, suggesting variations and extensions of known results. As an example, one might discuss the Cauchy functional equation $(f(x + y) = f(x) + f(y))$. To enrich the course and avoid undue emphasis in any one direction, several faculty members could participate. Topics which are not ordinarily treated in the standard courses might be introduced.

There are certain negative aspects of problem solving that should be mentioned. Every challenge carries with it the possibility of failure and subsequent discouragement. Perhaps the way to meet this is to have a variety of problems with a wide range of difficulty and to permit the student a great deal of choice. Competition cuts two ways, spurring some students on but depressing others. In some cases cooperation might be a good idea. There is some danger—small, I think—that a student might become a mathematical dilettante and waste his creative talents on "mere problem solving." For the prospective elementary or secondary school teacher that is not a fate worse than death. The likely effect would be to keep him mentally active and make him a better teacher. For the prospective mathematician it might be more serious, but I doubt it. There are many ways to love mathematics and to contribute to its development. Very few among us have earned the right to be snobbish and arrogant about the efforts of others, and even in the greatest these attributes are not very attractive.

Another possible drawback is that the time spent by a student on problem solving might be better used in the systematic study of some important discipline. It is debatable whether this is a valid objection. There is ample evidence that R. L. Moore's methods have produced many outstanding creative mathematicians. Rademacher's problem seminar, for many years a required course for graduate students at the University of Pennsylvania, has trained many generations in research and exposition. It is my own feeling that the habits of mind engendered by such methods far outweigh all other considerations.

All mathematicians are engaged in the solution of problems, in the widest sense of the word. In a narrower sense, a problem that is posed represents an outpost to be taken, a single engagement in our conquest of the unknown. It is no accident that the grand strategists of mathematics have been, with very few exceptions, superb tacticians.

■ *Florence D. Jacobson*

THE ROLE OF PROBLEMS IN THE DEVELOPMENT
OF MATHEMATICAL ACTIVITY

A great deal has been said about the need for "problems" in any mathematics curriculum. Books have been written on the subject of problems and problem solving and many experts contend that there is a great need to include more concrete problems in the present-day curriculum.

What is meant by "problem"? To some mathematicians this word means an application to the physical sciences, or a question arising from some other discipline outside of mathematics that can be answered using mathematical methods. To others, this might mean a research topic for a Ph.D. thesis in pure mathematics. Yet all would agree that it is the *active participation in mathematical activity* that is being sought. A "problem" must *involve the student;* he must *search* for the answer. Perhaps he will not reach his goal, but the search itself may prove more important than the goal.

The critics of the modern curriculum feel that the aim of teaching mathematics at the high school level should be "know-how." It is claimed that teaching problem solving will develop this "know-how." However, in order to solve problems, the student must learn mathematics.

Consider the teacher using problems and problem solving as a means of teaching. The first step in such a curriculum may be to teach the student to interpret the concrete problem in mathematical language. This requires an understanding of the vocabulary both of the mathematics and of the discipline from which the example is drawn. Let us suppose the student has reached the proper stage of comprehension and is able to interpret the problem in terms of mathematics. Perhaps his efforts will lead to the problem of solving a system of simultaneous equations. Fine! Now, how does the student find the solution if he has never had experience with simultaneous equations? Perhaps he guesses the correct answer for this particular problem. What learning experience will be carried over the next problem?

It is even possible that after attempting many problems of the same kind, some of the students will begin to understand the concepts involved. However, it would seem that it would be more realistic to use the problem to *motivate* the study of systems of simultaneous equations, rather than to expect the students to abstract the concept by solving many problems. The knowledge that systems of simultaneous equations arise from concrete situations would

101

make the subject more interesting to many students. The ability to handle such systems must be taught apart from the applications.

Professor Roy Dubisch in his book, *The Teaching of Mathematics*, cites as a common error in mathematics teaching "The failure to realize that training in reasoning is rather specific, so that reasoning cannot be done in any field without experience in that field."[1] Thus, for example, asking the student to solve problems in combinations and permutations without prior knowledge and experience in these topics would be useless.

However, once the theory has been taught and understood, the student is ready to tackle the problems. Now he can interpret his knowledge and apply it not only to the mathematical situation, but also to concrete examples. Problem solving is used to reinforce and to test the student's comprehension of a given topic. The student will profit greatly from such experience in problem solving. Not only will he convince himself and his teacher of his mastery of a certain concept, but he will be inspired by his success to try more difficult problems. The student who is unable to solve the problem will realize that he has not mastered the concept, whereas the better student will be able to see generalizations and perhaps will be able to pose new problems.

The use of problems to reinforce and to test the student's comprehension is recognized at all levels of mathematics instruction. The present-day text written for the advanced graduate student and even for the expert is apt to contain many problems. Many of these, of course, lead to further research; but is this not a generalization of this role of problems at the school level?

However, we would not include the routine exercises found in many textbooks at the school level in our discussion of problems. These are meant to evoke an automatic response on the part of the student. This is not to say that exercises which develop skills are unnecessary. Just as the musician must master technique in order to interpret successfully a musical composition, so must the mathematics student master technique if he is to use his knowledge with any hope of success. Such drill may also contain a degree of difficulty, and to the student it may offer some degree of satisfaction which is necessary to learning at any level. But the bright student will tire of this activity in a very short time, and even the average student will be bored if too much time and emphasis is demanded.

The great problems of mathematics have a place in the school curriculum. These are the problems that have served to create new fields of mathematical activity. Although greatness may be defined in terms of difficulty, it must also be defined in terms of impact upon mathematical development. The stories of the search for the solutions of such problems are fascinating to the student.

[1] Roy Dubisch and Vernon Howes, *The Teaching of Mathematics*, New York, John Wiley and Sons, Inc., 1963, p. 26.

102

The historical development of mathematics becomes exciting when presented in terms of unsolved or unsolvable problems. Challenging problems from the physical sciences as well as the famous problems of antiquity, the search for the solution of the general algebraic equation of degree n by means of rational operations and radicals, the development of non-Euclidean geometry as an outgrowth of the attempt to prove the dependence of the parallel postulate are all within the understanding of the high school student. I would cite the excellent discussion of these topics in *What Is Mathematics?* by Courant and Robbins[2], as a model for the use of great problems to trace the historical development of mathematics, as well as for motivation for the study of certain topics in the curriculum.

We may also examine the activity that is involved in problems and problem solving in another light. Since the most important aspect of problem solving for the high school curriculum is the personal involvement of the student, this can be achieved by what I shall call *problem activity*. That is, a problem need not be an application of a given concept to a concrete situation, nor the application of this concept to related mathematical situations. Any mathematical activity that causes the student to become an *active participant in the proceedings* is a problem activity, and a good curriculum employs such activities throughout.

The heuristic, or discovery, method of teaching in the classroom involves such activities. We would all agree that a student who discovers for himself will be more apt to understand and would be able to apply the concept. The problem activity should be part of any presentation of mathematics.

For example, this may be employed in a course using the axiomatic method in teaching. A teacher may wish to present a theorem and a proof to his class. He might enunciate the theorem and proceed to present the proof using the axioms and properties of the system under discussion. Presumably, enough background material has been presented and the students are familiar with deductive reasoning. If the proof is carefully presented, the class may follow the discussion. A good teacher would follow the presentation with an analysis of the proof, and he would try to involve the students in this analysis.

Instead of this procedure, the teacher could lead the students to *discover* the theorem based upon their previous experience and intuition. Perhaps he would lead the students to an abstraction from examples. Then, he would involve the students in a search for a proof. They would be lead to a step-by-step deductive argument that is the proof of the theorem. The student is part of the procedure from the very beginning. He induces from experience and proves by deduction. Both forms of activity are mathematical activity. Indeed, the student parallels the activity of the creative mathematician. However, the

[2] Richard Courant and Herbert Robbins, *What is Mathematics?*, New York, Oxford University Press, Inc., 1941.

student who is led to a conclusion by the inductive process and is not made aware of the need for the deductive proof is not doing mathematics.

Once the student has actively participated in the discovery of the proof, it becomes a part of him. The teacher or the textbook may finally display the proof as a logical entity for the student to see, to admire, to appreciate. This, too, is part of the mathematical experience. The use of problems and problem solving alone cannot make the student aware of the beauty of mathematics.

Although mathematics prior to the twentieth century was motivated to a great extent by problems in the physical sciences, the development of mathematics in this century has been in terms of mathematics itself.

"While several important changes have taken place since 1900 in our conception of mathematics or in our points of view concerning it, the one which truly involves a revolution in ideas is the discovery that mathematics is entirely independent of the physical world. To put this just a little more precisely, mathematics is now seen to have no necessary connections with the physical world beyond the vague and mystifying one implicit in the statement that thinking takes place in the brain."

The above quote is from an article by Professor Marshall Stone entitled "The Revolution in Mathematics."[3] He continues:

"When we stop to compare the mathematics of today with mathematics as it was at the close of the nineteenth century, we may well be amazed to note how rapidly our mathematical knowledge has grown in quantity and complexity, but we should also not fail to observe how closely this development has been involved with an emphasis upon abstraction and an increasing concern with the perception and analysis of broad mathematical patterns. Indeed, upon closer examination we see that this new orientation, *made possible only by the divorce of mathematics from its applications*, has been the true source of its tremendous vitality and growth during the present century. We realize, too, that the trend toward abstraction must inevitably continue, reinforced by the successes which are already to be credited to it. In following this trend and directing their attention more and more to the discernment and study of abstract patterns, mathematicians have become increasingly aware of the fundamental antithesis between the structural aspect of mathematics and the strictly manipulative aspect which so often appears to have paramount importance for the applications and so often is the principal preoccupation of the mathematics teacher." (The italics are mine.)

[7] Marshall Stone, "The Revolution in Mathematics," *American Mathematics Monthly,* Vol. 68, 1961, pp. 715–734.

Borrowing the argument of the proponent of concrete problems and problem solving, if the study of any discipline by a student is to parallel the historical development of that discipline, then the high school curriculum in mathematics must also develop "with an emphasis upon abstraction and . . . broad mathematical patterns."

Thus the role of problems in the mathematics curriculum must not be concerned only with the concrete applications used as motivation, nor with the mathematical and applied problems used to reinforce and to test the student's comprehension, but must also include the problem activity that may be used to develop an abstract pattern of thinking which is the need in mathematics today.

Finally, problems engender new problems—and this is mathematics. For ". . . we can only conceive of science as living, if besides solved problems, it has also unsolved ones, and if the answers to earlier questions lead to new questions and stimulate new research."[4]

[4] Heinrich Tietze, *Famous Problems of Mathematics*, Baltimore, Graylock Press, 1965, p. xv.

■ *Phillip S. Jones*

THE ROLE OF PROBLEMS IN SECONDARY
SCHOOL MATHEMATICS

The role of any item of content or of procedure depends upon two things, its potential value with reference to the goals of mathematical instruction, and the effectiveness with which the item is incorporated into the classroom teaching process. This latter statement does not deny the value of such extra-classroom activities as assigned homework, mathematics clubs and contests, and of the purely individual, unassigned, unscheduled work of the highly motivated able student. However, even most of these activities are largely rooted in teachers' stimuli and classroom activity.

The most common conception of the use of problems is not only a partial misconception (or at least too limited a view), but also the simplest illustration of the interaction between goals and classroom practices. If the goal is manipulative facility with an algorithm such as the multiplication of integers or the solution of quadratic equations, then the teaching procedures must also include some practice in the process, however strongly one insists that that meaning, understanding, rationalization should precede drill. Many persons and books loosely label these practice exercises as "problems." Others choose to regard a statement or situation as a *problem* only when it asks a question or defines an objective which cannot be answered or obtained by the immediate and direct application of processes known to the would-be problem solver. Admittedly, this definition implies that what is a problem for one student may not be one for another student. In application it could also lead to such niggling debates as whether finding the solution of $3z^4 - 4z^2 + 1 = 0$ is or is not a problem to a person who can solve $3x^2 - 4x + 1 = 0$. However, I believe that what is most important about the role of problems in teaching secondary school mathematics can be elaborated in terms of this definition, which, from now on, eliminates most of those necessary but unproblematic practice exercises from the domain of this discourse.

It is my belief that the major uses (goals) of problems are: (1) to interest or motivate, (2) to lead to "discovery" of processes or perception of inter-relationships, (3) to develop and practice "problem solving techniques", (4) to clarify the relationships between mathematics and the "worlds" of physical or social or psychological problems—that is, to clarify the idea of a mathematical model. This latter goal also includes an improved perception of the nature of a mathematical system—definitions, undefined terms, postulates,

106

and derived theorems. Goal (3) also implies some accompanying experience with logical reasoning.

It is less easy to classify clearly the types of problems and their methods of use. The sources of good problems, like gold, are where you find them! However, something can be said on each of these topics: goals, methods, types, sources. Perhaps it can be best said by giving some examples and a little of their history.

One of the most intriguing developments in the history of mathematics begins with a problem stated by Cardan who came close in his *Ars Magna* of 1545 to inventing complex numbers. After having expounded the solution of quadratic equations by completing the square, he proposed the problem: find two numbers whose sum is ten and whose product is 40. He said immediately, "Obviously this is impossible," but followed this statement with the suggestion "Never-the-less let us operate." By following the algorithm he found $5 + \sqrt{-15}$ and $5 - \sqrt{-15}$. He then checked this result by showing that these numbers satisfied the conditions of the problem, but ended by stating that to continue this would require a "new arithmetic which would be as subtle as it would be useless."

This story suggests not one but several problems for pedagogical use. It also suggests the history of mathematics as one source for problems. Cardan had prepared the way by his previous exposition of quadratics. Similarly today's teacher may use the problem, find two numbers whose sum is ten and product forty, as an addendum or challenge problem assigned along with more routine exercises. In this case the problem is intended to raise questions, even objections and debates, on the next day of class, and to set the stage for the introduction of complex numbers. Another teacher, or the same teacher on another day, may seek the same motivating, interest-getting goals by telling a little of Cardan and posing this problem for a class discussion, perhaps heuristically guided, and solution prior to any assignment.

An additional and even more open-ended problem is presented by Cardan's statement, without elaboration, that this is "obviously impossible." Given time and the problem setting, students can find several explanations, and even proofs, of this impossibility. They may discover the connection with the problem of finding the rectangle of maximum area with a given perimeter, or with the vertex of a parabola, or with the maximum of a quadratic function. In a lively class with a facile teacher, all of these may be "discovered" and interrelated by the class, along with a discussion of what "impossible" meant to Cardan and what it means in modern mathematics.

Cardan's "Never-the-less let us operate" can stimulate another discussion in what should be a continuing series of discussions with examples of how one extends mathematical ideas by such devices as analogy and trying formal processes in new situations, generalization and specialization, and by asking, "I wonder what would happen if?" Each of these discussions should be preceded, accompanied and followed by problems, mostly open-ended. It doesn't matter if some of them are trivial to a more sophisticated mathematician, and some should have no answer, or the answer "No." For example, after the class has studied congruence theorems for triangles, it would be a natural step and good to ask them if there are analogous congruence theorems for quadrilaterals. Their formulation, proof, and an analysis of their value (fruitfulness), or lack of value, are good problems leading toward such pedagogical goals as understanding of the nature of mathematics, mathematical creativity, and problem solving. There are many situations in all subjects and at all grade levels where such problems should be teased out of previous work. Thus when one has learned to circumscribe circles about triangles, he should be led to feel it natural to ask about circumscribing circles about quadrilaterals, to feel pleased rather than disconcerted when he discovers that it cannot be done—for all quadrilaterals. To find conditions under which this can be done then becomes a new problem.

These illustrations suggest the value of sequences of problems, planned—at least partially—by the teacher and leading toward the formulation of further problems, or a feeling for the necessity or appropriateness of a definition. A simple example of this latter is the classical process for motivating the extension of the definition of exponents from natural numbers to the rationals by presenting a sequence of exercises leading to a feeling for the appropriateness, so compelling as to almost be the necessity, that 3^0 be defined as 1.

It may be objected that such sequences are more nearly "exercises" than "problems." This may be more or less true depending upon the exercises themselves, not all sequences are merely successive computations, and also depending on the manner in which they are utilized in the teaching process. If the teacher leads the students to be aware of and searching for the ultimate goal of discovery, formulation, extension, these exercises are real problems.

Several recent text series, both experimental and commercial, have attempted to build in open-ended problems, inductive and developmental sequences, even heuristic questions so that the student who reads and thinks may have these experiences even when studying by himself. One series has even marked in exercise sets certain special problems upon which it bases the motivation or introductory ideas for the next developmental section. This latter is often introduced by a sequence of "Thinking Ahead" problems. The effectiveness of these devices seems to depend very highly upon the teacher. He must recognize their purposes and communicate them to his students. He must plan and take the time to use such problems properly. The writings of George Polya on heuristic methods and problem solving can be very helpful to teachers in this connection—and in the attempt to have pupils learn problem solving by solving problems.[1]

One recent series of textbooks deliberately includes some "open-ended" problems in each major section as well as special "For the Experimenter" problems which are intended to start students upon additional topics or extensions of old ones. The article "Mathematical Modes of Thought" by E. H. C. Hildebrandt suggests further procedures and values to be associated with the use of open-ended problems.[2]

"Sift, Sort, and Solve" is the heading used in one text for problems which are more or less genuine practical or "real-life" problems. In these the students must formulate the mathematical model of the situation and sort out essential data from some extraneous facts. The question of the role of practical problems and related question of "transfer of training" in the teaching of mathematics has long occupied psychologists and mathematics teachers. In 1922 Edward L. Thorndike wrote on this topic, noting that few textbook problems were important, real as opposed to "described," or genuine in the sense of arising as described and using data which would occur in life. Although in his view these shortcomings tended to invalidate these problems as providing students with either motivation or transferable training, he warned against the danger of becoming so involved with the scientific and other background needed to make problems real and genuine that the teaching of both mathematics and science suffers.[3]

More recently mathematicians and psychologists seem to feel that we need not depend solely on felt needs and immediate practicality for motivation and training in problem solving but that there is an intrinsic interest in both mathematics and problems which motivate and that, hopefully, a stress upon the "model" concept of the connections between mathematical structures and problems in other areas may provide a more effective basis for the future utilization of mathematics than has been revealed by earlier studies of transfer of training in secondary school mathematics. Recently simple linear programming problems have become popular. This is excellent, but many times writers have not squeezed out of them all the pedagogical values implicit in them by failing to stress and elaborate the model making processes and limitations of the problems.

The use of problems with special groups in clubs, seminars, contests, and in differentiated assignments for more able students is so obvious and well known as to need no further discussion. Similarly, it doesn't seem necessary to do more than enumerate the sources of problems in texts, contest problem books, books and journals dealing with recreations, and in the newer areas of application in the social, business, and management sciences as well as in the physical and biological sciences. The greatest needs seem to be for

109

increasing teacher imagination in the conception and use of open-ended problems and in the formulation and distribution of simple situations which use the process of model building, establishing correspondences between the elements, operations, and relations of a mathematical system and the essential elements of a conceptual, social, or physical system.

The foregoing exposition of the *purposes* for which problems may be used in secondary school mathematics, the *methods* for effecting this utilization, the *types* and *sources* of problems may, in conclusion, be further clarified by some historical notes on the role of problems in the teaching of mathematics.

The oldest written mathematics to come down to us are collections of problems. Our knowledge of Babylonian and Egyptian mathematics is all based upon analyses of problems rather than upon expositions of theory or proofs of theorems. It is conjectured that the Rhind papyrus, our major source of knowledge of Egyptian mathematics, was essentially a school copybook. It is interesting from the viewpoint of the present topic for several reasons. Not only does it contain a number of problems or exercises which are essentially the same and are largely drill work in successively more complicated manipulations, but it also contains what might be called "story problems," some of a genuinely practical nature, others of a pseudopractical character. Even some of the textbookishly practical problems involving measures of grain and land or division of inheritances appear contrived and more recreational than real when reconsidered. For example, there appears no genuine practical application of the Egyptian problem which called for determining the sides of two squares such that the sum of their areas was 100 and 3 times one side was 4 times the other. The same can be said of Babylonian tablet Plimpton 322 which presents a table of Pythagorean triples in such a way as to display a systematic construction for the triples with no apparent practical application in view. This supports a belief in the continuing motivational value of pure or theoretical problems which was even more extensively revealed in the famous Greek problems.

The story of the latter problems illustrates the growth and development of mathematical ideas over the centuries, points out the role of intellectual curiosity in this process and the values of working on even "impossible" problems. In fact the existence and nature of "impossible" and "unsolved" problems are less known and understood than they should be. Some presentation of them helps convey the cultural values and appreciations which are important goals, but hard to teach. All students should at least have been exposed to the "solution" of a problem by showing the simultaneous satisfaction of all its conditions to be impossible.

As with all problems, their pedagogical values will be realized only if their utilization is planned to do so. The mere lecture-discussion of trisection will

110

stimulate interest, but far greater dividends of motivation, discovery stimulated, practice in reasoning, analysis, and problem solving will be accrued by the teacher who directs and assists students to work on such questions as, "What angles can be exactly trisected?", the execution and proof of "illegal" trisections using "vergings" or mechanical devices, the search for and analysis of the nature of "illegal" procedures, etc. At such a time the presentation of some simply formulated but still unsolved problems such as the Goldbach Conjecture, or the existence of odd perfect numbers, helps to convey the idea that mathematics is still fascinatingly alive with many challenges and opportunities for interested and able students.

In the history of mathematics recurring discussions of the same problems, whether famous or not, help us to trace the influence of earlier writers and the threads of communication from antiquity to today. For example, one of the most persistently recurring discussions is that of the quadratic equation which we would write today as $x^2 + 10x = 39$. It is initially found in the algebra of Al-Khowarizmi (circa 825). He first told *how* to solve it by the process which we call "completing the square." Then in a later chapter he gave a "geometric proof" of this process using the diagram in which x^2 is represented by a square, $10x$ by two rectangles as shown, and a larger square of side $(x+5)$ and area 64 is finally completed by filling in the corner with a 5×5 square. This same problem occurs later in works by Abu Kamil, Al Kharki, and Leonard of Pisa.[4]

Today, this problem, its history, solution, and proof can be used to enhance instruction in such varying ways as to introduce the topic of quadratic equations or to suggest the method of completing the square, to create interest, to point out some of the multifold connections between algebra and geometry, or to illustrate model building again, this time within mathematics itself.

The varied use of challenge problems over the centuries is an interesting story for secondary school students. These range from serious contests between individual mathematicians, for example John of Palermo vs. Leonard of Pisa (13th century), and Tartaglia vs. Floridas (16th century) to the less formal, often nationalistic, letters published in the 17th and 18th centuries in such early journals as *Acta Eruditorum* and *The Transactions of the Royal Society* by Bernoulli, Euler, Newton, Leibnitz, and others, to the later prize contests announced by the French Academy which brought forth excellent and extensive memoirs. These problems were all more serious and more important than clearly recreational problems. However, they also have both their antiquity and their pedagogical uses. Recreational problems date back to the Greeks, Diophantos (1st century) and Metrodorus (circa 500), but first appeared in a printed collection in 1612 when the *Problèmes Plaisans et Délectables* of C. G. Bachet de Mèziriac was published. An interesting history of some problems and comments on their pedagogical use is to be found in *The History and Significance of Certain Standard Problems in Algebra* by Vera Sanford.[5] Problems have played a varied, important, and continuing role in the development of mathematics itself. They have played a similar role in the teaching of mathematics, but much can be done to capitalize further on their potential values and to test the beliefs of this writer and others that some of the intangible goals of stimulating interest, intuition, creativity, problem solving facility, and understanding of the model making process can be achieved through the improved use of problems.

[1] George Polya, *How to Solve It*, Princeton, N. J.: Princeton University Press, 1945. *Mathematical Discovery*, New York: John Wiley and Sons, Inc., Vol. I, 1962, Vol. II, 1965.

[2] E. H. C. Hildebrandt, "Mathematical Modes of Thought," Chapter 9 of *The Growth of Mathematical Ideas—Grades K-12*, Twenty-fourth Yearbook, National Council of Teachers of Mathematics, Washington, D. C., 1959.

[3] Edward L. Thorndike, "The Psychology of Problem Solving," *The Mathematics Teacher*, Vol. XV, 1922, pp. 212–227 and 253–264. This also appeared as Chapter V in Edward L. Thorndike, *The Psychology of Algebra*, New York: The Macmillan Company, 1928.

[4] L. C. Karpinski, "The Algebra of Abu Kamil," *The American Mathematical Monthly*, Vol. XXI, February 1914, p. 40.

[5] Vera Sanford, *The History and Significance of Certain Standard Problems in Algebra*, New York: Teachers College, Columbia University, 1927.

■ *Peter D. Lax*

THE ROLE OF PROBLEMS IN THE
HIGH SCHOOL MATHEMATICS CURRICULUM

I don't know of any reliable statistical study of the matter, but an overwhelming majority of my mathematical acquaintances became addicted to the subject in their high school years through the pleasures and pains of problem solving. It certainly loomed large in my early (age 13–15) education in Hungary, where the paramount role of problem solving in picking out talent and nurturing it was a cardinal principle. An eloquent description of that milieu is given by Gábor Szegö in his introduction to the *Hungarian Problem Book*.[1] The roster of problems there gives a good indication of what were regarded as suitable topics for high school students in those years: geometry was in, calculus was out; number theory, combinatorics and inequalities were popular.

With ambitious plans abounding to bring more and more advanced topics into the high school curriculum the old fare of problems has to be enlarged. How to do this imaginatively is a fascinating question; we can learn much from the Soviet Union, its Olympiads[2] and its special schools for talented youngsters under the leadership of Gelfand, Kolmogoroff and their circle. My impression is that in the United States problem solving is a declining art; in geometry this is no doubt due to a new style of texts which overemphasize the logical structure and underemphasize the more inventive aspects such as constructions. A peppery attack on this trend is launched in Wittenberg's article.[3]

There is, however, another more important role for problems in the high school curriculum, and that is to motivate the subject matter not only for those who have a special interest in mathematics and a special aptitude for it, but for all students. It is especially on the point of motivation that many recent American texts, claiming to be modern, fall down. In the pages which follow I would like to give a few examples of what I regard as proper motivation and an analysis, both psychologic and philosophic, of why so many new books go astray.

[1] SMSG, *Hungarian Problem Book* I, II, New Mathematical Library, Vol. 11, 12, Random House, New York.

[2] Izaak Wirszup, "The Fourth International Mathematical Olympiad for Students of European Communist Countries," *American Mathematical Monthly*, 1964, Vol. 71, pp. 308–316.

[3] Alexander Wittenberg, "Sampling a Mathematical Sample Text," *American Mathematical Monthly*, 1963, Vol. 70, pp. 452–459.

I will take my illustrations from the lower end of the high school curriculum: the multiplication of fractions and the multiplication of negative numbers, two somewhat dry subjects.

Let $\frac{a}{b}$ and $\frac{c}{d}$ be two fractions.

First Problem: What is the area of the rectangle with sides a/b and c/d?

Solution: The rectangle is made up of ac small rectangles with side lengths $1/b$ and $1/d$; therefore its area is ac times the area of the small rectangle. Since bd replicas of the small rectangles fill up a unit square, each small rectangle has area $1/bd$; therefore the original rectangle has area ac/bd.

In analogy with multiplication of integers we *define* the product of a/b and c/d to be the area of the rectangle, i.e., ac/bd. A virtue of this definition is that it furnishes geometric evidence for the distributive law (two rectangles with a common side can be put together to form a single larger rectangle).

Second Problem: How should the control center of a railroad reckon the average velocity of its trains along various portions of the track from reports of the times at which the trains pass stations along the line?

Solution: The average velocity v between the ith and jth station is

$$v = \frac{d_i - d_j}{t_i - t_j}$$

where d_i and d_j are the distances of stations i and j respectively from some arbitrary reference point along the rail line, and t_i and t_j are the times at which the train passed these stations. The interpretation of the quotient as velocity suggests the rules for carrying out division with variously signed quantities.

This example shows how making the right definition about arithmetic operations simplifies life: had we refused to operate with negative numbers we would have had to use four slightly different formulas, depending on which station reports an earlier time and how they are located with respect to the main station.

One can make a fairly good case for the distributive law on the basis of this definition; the commutative law however is better handled purely arithmetically.

The common feature of these two examples is that in both of them a certain problem outside of pure mathematics—calculation of areas, velocities—suggests a new concept and a new operation. Had we defined multiplication or division otherwise than we did, these operations would be *useless* for those particular applications; on the other hand if these new operations did not share the usual properties of multiplication and division, then we would be unable to

114

manipulate with them in the course of solving equations where we don't know in advance which of the variables will turn out to be positive, which negative.

There is an equally important second point to be made: making mathematical concepts and operations fit to deal with problems outside of mathematics is not merely a tribute that mathematics pays to the real world, but is a revitalizing source of new mathematics.

In contrast to this approach through problems, the current trend in new texts in the United States is to introduce operations with fractions and negative numbers solely as algebraic processes. The motto is: Preserve the Structure of the Number System. I find this a very poor educational device: how can one expect students to look upon the structure of the number system as an ultimate good of society? The main advantage claimed for this approach is that it displays uninterruptedly the logical structure of the number system. I am convinced that the logical structure per se is of no particular interest to the overwhelming majority of the school population, which is as it should be, and therefore that this approach will fail to hold the students' attention. True, in the logical approach there is occasion to present problems of deducing a conclusion from a given set of postulates; while some of these problems do have a certain appeal to the playful side of the human mind they fatally lack any element of surprise since conclusion and hypothesis are equally obvious. Therefore most students would find these problems artificial, mere exercises in hairsplitting, pedantry, the mountaining of mole hills. Of course I agree that many of the traditional problems of high school algebra are just as artificial, such as the ones involving perverse children who, instead of disclosing their age as asked, relate it in obscure ways to that of their brothers, sisters, parents, etc. The remedy is to stick to problems which arise naturally; to find a sufficient supply of these, covering a wide range, on the appropriate level is one of the most challenging problems for curriculum reformers.

My view of structure is this: it is far better to relegate the structure of the number system to the humbler but more appropriate role of a device for economizing on the number of facts which have to be remembered.

What motivates textbook writers not to motivate? Some, those with narrow mathematical experiences, no doubt believe those who, in their exuberance and justified pride in recent beautiful achievements in very abstract parts of mathematics, declare that in the future most problems of mathematics will be generated internally. Taking such a program seriously would be disastrous for mathematics itself; as Von Neumann points out in an article[4] on the nature of mathematics—the most perceptive ever written on the subject—it would

[4] James Newman, "The Mathematician," *The World of Mathematics*, New York, Simon and Schuster, 1956.

eventually lead to rococo mathematics. As philosophy it is repulsive since it degrades mathematics to a mere game. And as guiding principle to education it will produce pedantics, pompous texts, dry as dust, exasperating to those involved in teaching the sciences. If pushed to the extreme it may even cause the disappearance of mathematics from the high school curriculum along with Latin and the buffalo.

■ *H. O. Pollak*

ON INDIVIDUAL EXPLORATION
IN MATHEMATICS EDUCATION

When it was my good fortune to be allowed to participate in the SMSG ninth-grade writing team, I learned many things. I learned that it is a difficult challenge to put the material of the first year of algebra into a mathematically satisfying sequence. I learned that serious communication between secondary school teachers and a research mathematician is a very interesting and rewarding process. However, one of the lessons I learned, which I least expected to learn, was that without doubt the most difficult aspect of creating a good new textbook is to write a set of good problems. This is far harder than writing good text or teachers' commentary. The set of problems should progress slowly from very easy to more profound involvements of the most recent ideas in the course. It needs to provide the opportunity to gain skill without being boring. There must be occasional exercises that do not need the most recent work. There must be applications to other areas of mathematics and to subjects outside of mathematics. There must be the foreshadowing of ideas to come in the form of discovery exercises. It is probably impossible to do all of these in any one series; but it is necessary at least to try to think of all of these aspects. My experience in the one or two cases when I thought I came close to a good set of exercises is that it takes about a day of solid concentration to put such a set together.

If a course contains good text and teachers' commentary and good exercises in the above sense, this is wonderful, but it is still not enough. A major point of mathematical education is still missing. The exercises I have described above—in an idealized way, to be sure—can each be epitomized as follows: "Here is a problem—solve it;" or "Here is a theorem—prove it." Both of these are very important, but they fail to represent a third and crucial aspect of the matter: "Here is a situation—think about it." If one wishes to give an honest picture of what mathematics is really like, if one wishes to prepare the students for applications of the mathematics in the rich variety that is characteristic of the current work in engineering and in the social and physical sciences, and if one wishes to attach the best available pedagogic device to each classroom situation, then one must give the student the opportunity to explore for himself new situations, both within mathematics and outside mathematics.

It has often been said that once a mathematician knows what he is trying to prove, his job is half over. As the wealth of unsettled conjectures in mathematics indicates, this is an oversimplification. Many clearly formulated and clearly important theorems are waiting to be proved (or disproved). Nevertheless, it is the normal state of mathematical activity to have a situation that is crying out for understanding, and to be searching, patiently or otherwise, for the right way to look at this situation. No one denies this intuitive, discovery aspect of mathematics, but it is all too often deliberately excluded from our teaching. A carefully organized course in mathematics is sometimes too much like a hiking trip in the mountains that never leaves the well-constructed trails. The tour manages to visit a steady sequence of the high spots in the natural scenery. It carefully avoids all false starts, dead ends and impossible barriers and arrives by 5 o'clock every afternoon at a well-stocked cabin. The order of difficulty is carefully controlled, and it is obviously a most pleasant way to proceed. However, you miss the excitement of occasionally camping out or helping to find a trail and of making your way cross-country with only a good intuition and a compass as a guide. "Cross-country" mathematics is a necessary ingredient of a good education.

If this search for understanding in a new situation is an important but frequently unadmitted part of the activity of a *mathematician,* it is the bread and butter of the man who *applies* mathematics to other fields. Applications typically begin with an ill-defined situation outside of mathematics—in economics, or physics, or engineering, or biology, or chemistry, or geology, or almost any field of human activity. The job is to understand this situation as well as possible. The procedure is to make a mathematical model which will help to shed some light on the situation which we are trying to understand. Now the outside world is usually so complicated that we cannot subsume all its relevant features into the mathematical model and have any hope of doing anything with that model. We will have to leave things out—as few really important things as possible. The danger now comes in leaving out too much. For if we have discarded enough of the real world to obtain a tractable mathematical formulation, then the relevance of the results to the original situation may well have become suspect. This continual tug-of-war between the desire for mathematical simplicity and the fact of physical complexity is one of the most interesting features of applications of mathematics.

We have looked very briefly at two important and remarkably similar points, one relating to mathematics and the other to its applications. In both cases we have a situation which we are trying to understand, either within mathematics or without, and we are searching for the right way to look at it. Thus, "Here is a situation—think about it" is not only a fundamental activity, but also a *unifying* one, one which is common to all branches of mathematics and to all viewpoints in the spectrum from pure to applied. It is therefore very tempting to give students early and frequent experience with this kind of thinking. The opportunities are numerous and the pedagogic advantages great. Finding the

118

right way to look at a situation can be an exciting activity, with intense personal involvement and interaction for the whole class, and can truly give the student a sense of participation and discovery in mathematics.

Outstanding among the recent efforts to think deeply about the mathematics curriculum is the report of the Cambridge Conference on School Mathematics, "Goals for School Mathematics," which has paid particular attention to the need for personal mathematical exploration.* At the risk of repeating some of the thoughts which can be found in the Cambridge Report, it is perhaps worthwhile to give some random examples of opportunities for encouraging such exploration.

Fairly early in the elementary school, students have to learn the multiplication table. It can sometimes be very helpful to ask them to do the multiplication table backwards. "Give me a problem whose answer is 14. Give me one whose answer is 15; one for 16; another one. Give me a problem whose answer is 17. What do you mean, you can't? . . ." In this way the student may first discover that when you look at numbers multiplicatively they are not all alike.

In connection with the teaching of measurement, it may be instructive for the students to think about the properties they would like their units to have. If you are measuring the length of various small objects in the classroom, or the size of the room itself, or the distance you walked to school in the morning, or the length of a weekend excursion, is it convenient to use the same units to talk about each? If not, what would you like the relation between units to be? The students could invent units, say for the problem of measuring the length of the room. If one of them should suggest that a room length would be a good unit, the answer is "Fine. Now what is the width of the room in that unit?"

In the secondary school, especially in connection with plane geometry, the students are likely to see a small but interesting collection of distinct right triangles. Besides the isosceles right triangle and the $30°$, $60°$, $90°$ one, there are the simple Pythagorean triples on which most homework problems are built: $(3, 4, 5)$, $(5, 12, 13)$, $(8, 15, 17)$, $(7, 24, 25)$—and that is probably all. It is very natural for the student to ask whether there are any more. The first response may well be "Of course. After all, there are $(6, 8, 10)$, $(30, 40, 50)$, and so forth." You discover that that isn't what you meant. You would like the elements to be relatively prime. The next fact that the student might come to observe is that the difference between two consecutive squares is always an odd number, and that every odd number appears as the difference of two consecutive squares. Therefore, every odd square appears as the difference of two

* Published for Educational Services, Incorporated by Houghton Mifflin Company, Boston, 1963. See especially pp. 11, 73–76, 80–81.

consecutive squares. This now shows that there is an infinity of possible examples. Do we have all of them? No, because $(8, 15, 17)$ is not covered by the algebraic relation for consecutive squares:

$$(2n^2 - 2n)^2 + (2n - 1)^2 = (2n^2 - 2n + 1)^2$$

More generally, however, this looks like the relation:

$$(x^2 - y^2)^2 + (2xy)^2 = (x^2 + y^2)^2$$

Now do we have all of them? How do we pick pairs of x and y so as to obtain all of them just once? It will be very interesting for the students to investigate this relation between geometry and elementary number theory and algebra. There are, of course, many other directions in which this particular exploration can go. Later on, for example, it can be extended to complex numbers and Gaussian integers.

If you continue the questions raised by the isosceles right triangle into elementary trigonometry, the student may begin to wonder when the simple trigonometric functions turn out to be algebraic expressions. The half-angle and sum and difference formulas give you a number of examples when you start from $30°$ and $45°$, and the student will discover a great deal of interesting technique in simplifying some of the resulting algebraic expressions. The theory of the pentagon allows you to put in many more interesting cases, since

$$\sin 18° = \frac{\sqrt{5} - 1}{4}.$$

We can now make a table of the trigonometric functions, for, say, every $1\frac{1}{2}°$ rationalized into their nicest form. Can any denominator with a finite number of radicals always be rationalized?

Just as the normal mathematics curriculum abounds in opportunities for personal mathematical exploration, so the world around the student is full of everyday situations which he can attempt to understand, to varying degrees, in a mathematical way. It is of course not possible to predict, when you start, how difficult a model for a particular situation is likely to be. However, it is great fun to try. Again we must be content with a few random examples; the ones which follow happen to concern questions of city traffic.

Suppose that in a city with a rectangular network of streets (Manhattan geometry) you wish to walk from one point to another not on the same street. At each corner there are two sensible directions in either of which you are willing to go. None, one, or both of these directions are controlled by the traffic light.

120

If both are controlled by the traffic light (as at A), you obviously go the way the light is green. If one direction is controlled by a light and this light is green (as might be at B), or if neither is controlled by a light (as at C), you have a real choice as to which way to go. What is the optimal strategy for reaching your destination in minimum time? How much do you have to assume about traffic lights, length of blocks, etc.? In a more general geometry, and if you are traveling by car, what other criteria for optimality of a route might you consider—minimum distance, minimum number of traffic lights, minimum number of intersections at which you do not have the right of way?

On city streets it is normal to require cars to park in certain regular and clearly defined parking spaces. Suppose you allow cars to park at random in any space large enough for them. How much space would be wasted by such a procedure?

What is the best speed to permit cars to travel in a tunnel? The crucial fact here is that, based on a fixed human reaction time, the safe distance between successive cars is roughly a quadratic function of the speed. If you set the speed limit very low, then the cars will be very close together, but it will take each of them a very long time to get through the tunnel. If you set the speed limit too high, then each car gets through the tunnel quite rapidly, but does the distance between cars become so large that very few of them get through? What is an appropriate criterion for success anyway?

Hundreds of similar examples can easily be found from many different situations in life, and, as we have noted previously, the making of mathematical models of such situations is the heart of applied mathematics. We should also consider the process by which such opportunities for exploration of both mathematical and nonmathematical situations can be brought into the classroom. How can we persuade teachers to use this pattern of instruction when the opportunity arises? There are several difficulties here which must be over-

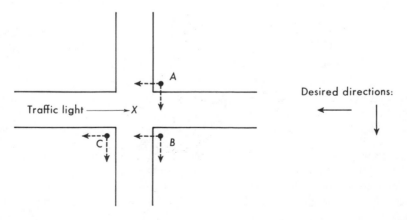

come.   First of all, many teachers of mathematics have never been involved in the process of building mathematical models of situations in the outside world. Prospective teachers need an opportunity to participate in such model building themselves in order to broaden their view of mathematics and in order to give the necessary experience.   An experimental course is now being prepared by the Committee on the Undergraduate Program in Mathematics of the Mathematical Association of America in which situations from economics, biology, engineering, physics, etc., are first comprehended and then explored mathematically.   If this course is successful, it will provide teachers not only with the necessary experience, but also with a source of interesting models to bring into their own classrooms.   Secondly, if we wish the classroom presentation to include an occasional "Here is a situation—think about it" in addition to "Here is a problem—solve it" and "Here is a theorem—prove it," then the prospective teacher should have been exposed to this kind of teaching in his own college career.   We cannot very well expect someone to teach in this style if it has never been done to him.   It would, therefore, be very reasonable for us to provide opportunities for individual exploration also in our university mathematics courses, where they are probably even greater than in the elementary and secondary school.   We have to admit, however, that any attempt of the student to understand a situation for himself is often in conflict with the pedagogic style of university mathematics instruction.   By providing the opportunities for the exploration of both mathematical and nonmathematical situations in connection with mathematics courses, we can not only resolve this conflict, but also help to give each student the breadth of mathematical experience which his education must, in fact provide.

■ *George Polya*

ON TEACHING PROBLEM SOLVING

In what follows, I am concerned, in the first place, with the teaching of mathematics in the average United States high school. Yet this article should contribute to an international dialogue. Therefore, I shall emphasize such points as are applicable (at least approximately) "on the high school level," that is, to college-bound young people of ages 12 to 18 anywhere; for example, to students of a Central-European "Gymnasium" or "Lycée."

Other limitations of the scope of this article which are all in the nature of things will be carefully emphasized, each in its place, in the following.

1. *Art, not science.* Obviously, teaching is not an exact science with a widely accepted precise terminology. Therefore, the aims and methods of teaching cannot be adequately discussed without carefully and extensively described concrete examples. The space allotted to this article excludes detailed examples; I must refer for fuller explanations and appropriate illustrations to my books, which are also available in translations.[1]

Teaching is a complex human performance largely dependent on the personalities involved and on local conditions. There is no science, properly so called, of teaching today, and there will hardly be such a science in the foreseeable future. Especially, there is not one demonstrably best teaching method— as there is not one demonstrably best way to play a Beethoven sonata. There are as many good teaching methods as there are good teachers: teaching is more an art than a science. (This does not mean, of course, that teaching cannot benefit by judicious attention to psychological experiments and theories.)

At any rate, what follows is a nondogmatic presentation of my personal convictions. I shall be glad if any open-minded administrator or teacher can retain from it some points which suit the conditions of his school or his personal taste.

2. *Aims.* The aims of teaching, the subjects to be taught, and the methods to be used depend on the conditions prevalent at such and such location at such and such time: they should satisfy the needs of the community and are limited by the availability of teaching personnel and facilities. (They depend in prac-

---

[1] *How to Solve It*, Second Edition, Garden City, Doubleday and Co., Inc., 1957. *b. Mathematics and Plausible Reasoning*, Vols. 1 and 2, Princeton University Press, 1954. *c. Mathematical Discovery, on Understanding, Learning and Teaching Problem Solving*, New York, John Wiley & Sons, Inc., Vol. 1, 1962, Vol. 2, 1965.

Translations (if still in the press at this writing, the letter is in parentheses): Arabic *a*; French *a, b, (c)*; German *a, b, (c)*; Hebrew *a*; Hungarian *a, (c)*; Japanese *a, b, c*; Yugoslav *a*; Polish *a*; Roumanian *b*; Russian *a, b*.

tice not directly on local conditions, but on the more or less enlightened evaluation of these conditions by the local authority.)

Yet we cannot meaningfully discuss teaching without having a definite aim in mind. It is my personal conviction that the principal task of mathematics instruction on the high school level is to teach those young people to THINK.

Whatever I shall say in the sequel springs from this basic conviction. If the reader cannot share my conviction fully, I hope that he can share it to some extent, that he can regard as a major subordinate aim what for me is the principal aim, and then he may find useful suggestions in the following.

Of course, I do not forget essential supplementary aims—I just think that they are well compatible with what I regard as the principal aim. Such supplementary tasks are: to prepare all students for the physics course if such a course is a part of the high school curriculum; to prepare future engineers and scientists for college. As regards the future mathematicians, there is one very important point: they should not be disgusted by ill-directed teaching. Yet to introduce such subjects as have interest only for future mathematicians is superfluous—and unfair to the great majority of students.

3. *Think.* I said that the principal aim of the mathematics curriculum on the high school level is to teach the students to think. This statement needs further explanation, but an adequate explanation would necessitate repeating a substantial fraction of the examples treated in my books quoted above, in footnote 1. Such repetition is out of the question, but the following hints may help.

There have been proposed various objectives from various sides for the teaching of mathematics on the high school level such as the following: experience in independent thinking, improved working habits, desirable mental attitudes, broadening of outlook, mental maturity, introduction to the scientific way of thinking. It seems to me that these objectives, when concretely and reasonably interpreted on the high school level, are largely overlapping and cover jointly the aim that I have in mind.

Approaching from another side, we can get a more definite picture. Our teaching should encompass all principal aspects of the mathematician's thinking as far as feasible on the high school level. The most conspicuous activities of the mathematician are discovering strict proofs and building axiomatic systems. Yet there are other activities which usually leave little trace on the mathematician's finished published work and so are less conspicuous, but not less important such as extracting a mathematical concept from, or recognizing it in, a concrete situation, and then "guessing" in many forms, anticipating the result, and anticipating the great lines of the proof before the details are filled in. Such "guessing" may involve generalizing from observed cases, inductive reasoning, arguments from analogy, etc.

If the teaching of mathematics gives only a one-sided, stunted idea of the mathematician's thinking, if it totally suppresses those "informal" activities of guessing and extracting mathematical concepts from the visible world around us, it neglects what may be the most interesting part for the general student, the most instructive for the future user of mathematics, and the most inspiring for the future mathematician.

4. *Active learning.* "For efficient learning, the learner should discover by himself as large a fraction of the material to be learned as feasible under the given circumstances."[2] I prefer this statement of the "principle of active learning" which is the least controversial and oldest educational principle (we may trace it back to Socrates). Mathematics is not a spectator sport: it cannot be enjoyed and it cannot be learned without active participation, and so the principle of active learning is particularly important for us mathematics teachers, especially if we regard as our principal aim, or one of our major aims, to teach the students to think.

If we wish to develop the student's mentality we must be careful to let first things come first. Some activities come to him more easily and more naturally than others: guesses more easily than proofs, solving concrete problems more naturally than building up conceptual structures. In general, the concrete comes before the abstract, action and perception before words and concepts, concepts before symbols, and so on.

As the student should learn not passively, but by his own effort, let us start there where the effort is less and the goal of the effort more understandable from the student's standpoint: the student should become familiar with the concrete before the abstract, with the variety of experience before the unifying concept, and so on.

This leads up to the solution of mathematical problems which is, in my opinion, the mathematical activity nearest to the center of everyday thinking. We have a problem when we seek means to an end. When we have a desire that we cannot immediately satisfy we think of means to satisfy it and so we have a problem. Most of our thinking which is not mere daydreaming is concerned with things we want to get and with means of getting them, that is, with problems.

Everyday problems often lead to simple mathematical problems, and the step of abstraction from the everyday to the mathematical problem can be made easy and natural for the student with a little skill on the part of the teacher. And as everyday problems are at the center of our everyday thinking, mathematical problems can be expected to be at the center of the teaching of mathematics.

The solution of problems was the backbone of mathematical instruction since the time of the Rhind Papyrus. The work of Euclid can be considered as a pedagogical achievement, dissecting the great subject of geometry into

[2] Ibid., Vol. 2, page 103.

manageable problems. The solution of problems is, in my opinion, still the backbone of the teaching of mathematics on the high school level—and I am embarrassed that such an obvious thing needs to be emphasized.

Certainly, there are other things that also should be presented at the high school level: mathematical proofs, the idea of an axiomatic system, perhaps even a glimpse at the philosophy behind mathematical proofs and structures. Yet these things are much farther away from everyday thinking and cannot be appreciated or even understood without a sufficient background of mathematical experience which the student acquires mainly by solving mathematical problems.

5. *Classification of problems.* There are problems and problems, and all sorts of differences between problems. Yet the difference which is the most important for the teacher is that between "routine" and "nonroutine" problems. The nonroutine problem demands some degree of creativity and originality from the student, the routine problem does not. The nonroutine problem has some chance, the routine problem has practically no chance, to contribute to the mental development of the student. The line of demarcation may not be sharp, but the extreme cases are clearly recognizable. The space allotted allows only a brief description of two types of routine problems, the "one-rule-under-your-nose-problem" and the "just-vocabulary-problem."

A problem can be solved by straightforward mechanical application of a rule, and the student has no difficulty to find out of which rule: the rule is thrust under his nose by the teacher or the textbook. No invention, no challenge to the intelligence of the student is involved, and what he can benefit from such a "one-rule-under-your-nose-problem" is just a little practice in the application of that one rule, an isolated little bit of mechanical knowledge.

A question is designed to check whether the student can correctly use a recently introduced term or symbol of the mathematical vocabulary; the student can answer the question right away if he has understood the explanation of the term or symbol; not a spark of invention, no challenge to his intelligence is involved—it is just a vocabulary question.

Routine problems, even of the two kinds just described, may be useful or even necessary if administered at the right time in the right dose. What I am against are overdoses of routine problems by which the intelligent students may become disgusted with the stuff that is presented to them under the label "mathematics."

"Traditional" textbooks are harshly criticized nowadays, but most of the critics do not seem to notice what is usually, in my opinion, their weakest point: almost all their problems are one-rule-under-your-nose-problems.

"Modern" textbooks often have chapters full of new terms and symbols which remain unrelated to the experience and background of the student and of which, therefore, the student cannot make serious use. And so the prob-

126

lems at the end of the chapter are particularly flat routine problems, most of them just vocabulary questions. It seems to me that the disservice to students is in both cases of the same quality.

I shall not explain what is a nonroutine mathematical problem: if you have never solved one, if you have never experienced the tension and triumph of discovery, and if, after some years of teaching, you have not yet observed such tension and triumph in one of your students, look for another job and stop teaching mathematics.

6. *Choice of problems.* The solution of a nonroutine problem may demand genuine effort from the student. Yet he will not make the effort if he is not motivated to make it. The best motivation is interest in the problem. Therefore, we must take the greatest care to choose interesting problems and make them attractive.

First of all, the problem must appear *meaningful and relevant from the student's viewpoint.* It must be naturally connected with things that are familiar and serve a purpose that is comprehensible to the student. If the problem appears irrelevant to the student, the teacher's word that it will be important later is but a poor substitute.

Not only the choice, but also the presentation, of the problem deserves our care. A good presentation brings out connections with familiar things and renders the purpose more comprehensible. The principle of active learning suggests a useful little teaching trick: the teacher should not begin with a full statement of the problem, but with an appropriate suggestion and should let the students find the final formulation.

Now and then the class should work at a more significant problem that has a rich background and may serve as a gateway to a whole chapter of mathematics. And the class should work at such a "research problem" without hurry so that, according to the principle of active learning, the student should discover (should be led to discover) the solution and explore some implications of the solution by themselves. This is a first glimpse of what Wagenschein calls "paradigmatic teaching."

7. *Leading to discover.* The idea should be born in the student's mind and the teacher should act only as midwife. The metaphor is old (is due to Socrates) but not obsolete. If we regard improving the student's mind as the principal, or a major, aim of teaching mathematics on the high school level, and the student's work in solving mathematical problems as the principal, or a major, means to this end, leading the student to discover the solution must appear as the principal, or a major, concern of the mathematics teacher.

And the very first point about helping the student to the solution is not to help him too much: he should do as much as possible by himself. The teacher should act as midwife to the idea—and avoid too much interference with the natural process of birth.

Less metaphorically, in helping the student, the teacher should offer only *inside help,* that is, such suggestions as *could have occurred to the student himself,* and avoid *outside help,* that is, telling bits of the solution which have no relation to the student's state of mind.

I say that it is important, I do not say that it is easy, to give inside help. To give it efficiently, the teacher must know very well both the problem and the student; moreover, he must be experienced and familiar with such steps of problem solving as occur often and naturally.

8. *Heuristics.* Heuristics is the study of the ways and means of discovery and invention. It studies especially such steps of problem solving that occur often and naturally and have some chance to bring us nearer to the solution. It is not a too usual kind of study, although Descartes and Leibnitz meditated on it (the latter called heuristics the "Art of Invention"), the subject was practically dead when my first paper on it was printed in 1919.

For more information about heuristics (problem solving, guessing, . . .) see the references in footnote 1. The simplest ideas of heuristics are the most important for the teacher, who could, in fact, extract them from his own experience by himself as they are a matter of mere common sense. (But common sense is rath uncommon, as Descartes observed.)

Here is a piece of advice about everyday problems which may seem to you utterly trivial. Face your problem if you want to solve it; ask yourself: *What do I want?* And, when your mind is made up and your purpose is set, take stock of the things at your disposal which you could use to attain it; ask yourself: *What have I?* Having surveyed for some time the things you have some chance to use, you may return to your first question and develop it: *What do I want? What kind of thing do I want? How can I get this kind of thing? Where can I get it?* And so asking, you may get closer to the solution of your problem.

It is less trivial to observe that everyday problems are analogous to mathematical problems in certain respects. The teacher, trying to give inside help to a student engaged in the quest of the unknown of some high school math problem, can appropriately use the above questions, or parallel questions, expressed in mathematical terms.

The teacher asks: *What do you want? What is the unknown?* If the object of his quest, the unknown, is sufficiently clear to the student, the teacher may go on: *What have you? What are the data? What is the condition?* If the student gives sufficiently clear answers to these questions too, the teacher may return to his initial question and develop it: *What do you want? What is the unknown? How can you get this kind of unknown? By what data can you determine this kind of unknown?* And these questions have a good chance to mobilize relevant knowledge in the student's mind and bring him closer to the solution.

The questions: *What do you want? What have you? How can you get this kind of thing? What is the unknown? What are the data? What is the condition? By what data can you determine this kind of unknown?* are specimens of a lowbrow, practical, common sense heuristics. The teacher should use these questions first in cases where they easily suggest the right idea to the student. Then he should use them in more and more cases, as often as he can use them with judgment and tact. Eventually, the student may get the point and learn to use these questions by himself: He learns so to *direct his attention to essentials* when facing a problem. And so he has acquired a habit of orderly thinking which is the greatest possible benefit that the majority of students, who will never use technical mathematics in their profession, can derive from the high school mathematics class.

Teachers who would like to know more about heuristics are directed once more to footnote 1.

■ *Paul C. Rosenbloom*

PROBLEM MAKING AND PROBLEM SOLVING

I. *Introduction*

We regard problem solving as the basic mathematical activity. Since, in mathematical education, our first concern must be with what we want the student to do, we must focus our attention on this domain.

Other mathematical activities such as generalization, abstraction, theory building, and concept formation are based on problem solving.

For example, after we have learned how to find a function whose derivative is a given polynominal, the question arises of finding for any given function g a function f such that $f' = g$. How far can we carry this? For which functions g is there a solution? How can we find f? What data determine f? Can we estimate f without computing it? Can we approximate f to within a given error? The whole process of generalization to the concept of the integral is based on tackling problems such as these.

The abstract concept of a field grew out of the question of what properties were really essential to the results of Kummer and Dedekind on algebraic numbers. The problem arose of whether one could prove these results on the basis of such and such assumptions.

The construction of a theory usually breaks down into the solution of a sequence of problems. Consider the theory of systems of linear equations. What simple systems are easy to solve? Can we transform any given system into one of these simple systems? What is the complete set of solutions? When does there exist a solution? When is it unique? Often, in the exposition of a theory, this process of development is hidden, and the results are presented in such a way that the reader is unaware of what problems the theory solves or how anyone thought of the particular theorems which are proved.

A definition is usually presented as God given, with no indication as to why one should introduce the particular concept, or why one defines it in a particular way. Actually, the definitions and concepts which have survived historically are the ones which met specific needs growing out of the investigation of problems. For example, the modern concept of function is an outgrowth of the question of what objects are represented by Fourier series and the question of for what objects are the usual results of elementary calculus valid.

Problem solving and problem making play a fundamental role in teaching and curriculum writing, programed instruction, and testing.

Research into problem solving sheds important light on the mathematical and psychological problems of mathematical education.

One of the main social functions of the mathematics curriculum is to teach

130

one of the principal methods of acquiring new knowledge. To find out whether we are achieving this objective, we must see whether the student can solve problems for which he has received no specific instruction.

People like Polya have begun to analyze the strategies of problem solving and have begun to present exercises on the relevant strategies. Still, for the most part, we leave the acquistion of these strategies mostly to experience, unsystematically organized and largely unanalyzed.

Several investigators have begun experiments on the explicit teaching of problem solving. This ranges from the inquiry training by Suchman on the techniques of asking good questions to the programed instruction in problem-solving techniques by Klamkin and Hively, conducted at the Minnesota National Laboratory. The research is still in progress, and we do not know yet how effectively problem solving can be taught explicitly.

II. Teaching and Curriculum Writing

After ten years of intensive experience in experimental teaching and curriculum writing, I am gradually tending toward the approach of Polya and Szegö and R. L. Moore. After I decide what I want to teach, I begin writing the problems which I want the student to work on. I try to arrange these in a sequence and break them up into steps so as to lead the student to develop for himself the mathematics I want him to learn.

Then I begin writing the introductory expository material, but try to keep this to a minimum. My main object in this expository material is to build up in the student's mind a *gestalt* of what the whole problem complex is about, why it is important, and how we are led to the devices which are employed, before I immerse the student in the details.

The expository material also serves to summarize and clinch the ideas developed in the preceding set of problems, and to formulate and define precisely the concepts to which we have been led.

In my teaching I tend to start with problems with a minimum of new terminology. I ask the students questions but rarely tell them anything. In a course the main classroom activity is discussing the students' homework.

When I decide to teach something I ask myself what specific problems can I give which will lead the student to learn what I want him to learn. Or what "baby research" problems is the student prepared to tackle. Then I ask myself how I can adapt these problems to my target audience.

For example, several years ago I was asked to teach a demonstration class of second graders who knew only addition and subtraction. I decided to introduce them to the problem of partitions: how many ways can a given integer be represented as a sum of integers; such as
$$5 = 5 + 0 = 4 + 1 = 3 + 2 = 3 + 1 + 1 = 2 + 2 + 1 = 2 + 1 + 1 + 1 = 1 + 1 + 1 + 1 + 1.$$
Then I devised the story of Lower Slobbovia, where the people have only

pennies and 2-cent pieces and asked how many ways a Slob can make a given amount of money into change.

In line with Piaget's suggestion that children form their spatial concepts in the order topological, projective, then metric, a number of us have been introducing the idea of a curve early in the curriculum. This is usually done quite didactically without giving any reason for studying objects. Usually the only property discussed is the Jordan curve theorem, which is an embedding property depending on the curve's being in a plane. I have observed that the teaching of such material tends to be excessively verbal.

Being dissatisfied with out MINNEMAST (Minnesota Mathematics and Science Teaching Project) material as well as that of others, I began searching for an approach centered around a problem, with an emphasis on intrinsic properties which would be valid for space curves as well. So this year I have begun presenting kindergarten children with string figures, such as:

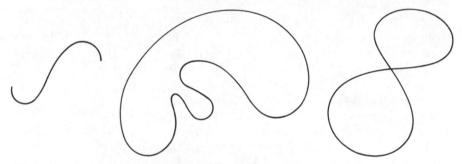

I ask them, if you cut this figure any place, how many pieces do you get? Try this with scissors and see for yourself. Does it make any difference where you cut it? Try some experiments.

Compare with a piece of paper. Remove a point, or two, or ten points (prick it with a needle). Now how many pieces do you get?

After a good period of experimentation, the children begin to classify objects with respect to cut-point properties. Only *then* do I introduce the term curve.

I may imbed the problem in the story of an intelligent worm who wants to find out what kind of world he is living on.

III. Programed Instruction

I am not convinced of the general utility of programed instruction, and I agree with Kenneth May that most published programed material in mathematics is actually harmful. But I think that programed instruction is a powerful vehicle for learning pedagogy and would advocate exercise in programing as a normal component of methods courses.

It is invaluable for a prospective teacher to be forced to define the objectives of a lesson precisely, devise a sequence of tasks into small enough

132

steps, try out early versions on individuals, refine the program, and finally arrive at an effective and precisely defined lesson.

In order to make up good problems to incorporate as items in the program, he must analyze the steps and skills required to solve a particular problem and must consider how a student can be led to think of any device or technique required.

After such exercise the student teacher will be much better prepared to handle the learning problems of a whole class by more informal procedures.

IV. Test Construction

In the evaluation of learning we must obtain samples of the student's mathematical behavior. We must define precisely the objectives of a given course or unit of instruction, and then devise tasks which will require the student to exhibit the behavior we are interested in, if it is in his repertoire.

When we define the objectives behaviorally, we must make a task analysis. This is usually difficult for the objectives which we consider most significant.

Having made such a task analysis, we must then devise items, that is, problems which test whether the student can perform the given task.

It is rare that a problem tests a single ability. Even such a simple problem as "Solve the equation $2x^2 + 7x - 9 = 0$," tests several abilities and, since it can be solved in several ways, the student's answer doesn't tell you which abilities he exhibited. The problem "What is the last digit in the decimal numeral for $(7^7)^7$?" tests a more complex set of abilities.

So it is extremely unlikely that we will be able to make a task analysis of the objectives and then devise a test consisting of "pure" items, each of which tests for a particular ability. The task analysis helps us to be sure to include items testing all relevant objectives. But it remains to analyze the test by classifying the items according to what they test and then construct a description of the information which the test yields.

In spite of considerable research it is still not clear what a test measures. It seems likely that the result of a test should be described by a multidimensional vector. But the components seem to have a geometrical structure which is not fully understood. We regard the research of Guttman as a promising direction in the analysis of tests.

Incidentally, most test constructors are neither good enough mathematicians nor good enough psychologists to make good tests.

V. Investigation Teaching of Problem Solving

We can learn a great deal from the work of Simon, Newell, Shaw, and others on programing problem solving for computers. This requires us to specify what problem-solving behavior consists of precisely enough for an idiot to perform the work. This type of specification would be extremely helpful to use for both teaching and testing.

Inasmuch as Church's theorem shows that there exist no algorithms for solving all problems in elementary number theory, no finite program can include all effective problem-solving strategies. It may be feasible, however, to program enough representative strategies to give us a clear task analysis for test construction purposes, as well as insight into the problems of teaching other strategies which do not lend themselves to such precise formulation.

A program for a heuristic gives us a precise definition of the behavior we should look for in testing problem-solving ability. Since, anyway, in test construction we can hope, at best, only to sample from an infinite pool of potential items, it is sufficient for our purposes to obtain programs for a sample of all strategies.

A crucial problem in this area is: what does it mean to know a structure? Although several leaders have recently been advocating that we teach structures rather than isolated facts and skills, no one has given a behavioral definition of the mastery of a structure. Thus, we still have little more than vague intuition to guide us in teaching and testing.

I conjecture that the difference between knowing a structure and not knowing it is essentially a matter of aesthetic judgment. Many of us know how it feels inside when we recognize beauty. The question is what difference does the appreciation of beauty make in a person's behavior. Can we specify some sequences of tasks which improve a person's judgment of a work of art? (A mathematical proof, the solution of a problem, and the construction of a theory are all works of art.) Can we train a computer to be an art critic?

As we make progress in the programing heuristics, we can begin the explicit incorporation of the teaching of problem solving into the curriculum. Some starts have been made in this direction, but the field is still virgin territory. This whole area will probably be an extremely fruitful one for people engaged in research and development in mathematical education.

■ *František Wolf*

PROBLEMS IN THE TEACHING OF MATHEMATICS

In this short paper we want to discuss open questions and some facts grouped around the use of problems in the teaching of mathematics. If we use a broad enough definition we can say that doing mathematics is solving problems.

There are several types of mathematical problems. The best known and the most important are the problems which test comprehension and are used as practice for certain mathematical techniques. We would prefer to call those exercises. The students are usually handed a recipe. An exercise is demonstrated on the board. Then they are asked to solve several others which are often identical except for numerical data. Their difficulty can be measured by the number of steps which they require.

Next, we present the student with an exercise whose solution requires a technique or procedure with which he is already familiar. The main hurdle which the student has to overcome is to recognize the situation which calls for a particular technique, or better, he has to fit to a particular situation the appropriate technique. But he has learned many techniques, so he has a choice and has to recognize which particular one is effective. He has to match the problem with hundreds of procedures, just like trying keys in a stubborn lock, twisting the keys in different ways, trying to decide whether the resistance is due to a rusty lock or to the inadequacy of the key.

This "selection and fitting of keys" is a fundamental thought pattern. It has been built into computers and it occurs very essentially in all mathematical research, from the most elementary stages to the most creative levels.

Mathematics seems inconceivable without problems. When a chapter has been explained, introducing a set of new ideas, neither the student nor the teacher knows whether all this did sink into the pupil's mind, whether he connected all the threads which bind it to older material. The only way to check it is by working problems. It is not unusual that the more intelligent students ask for it themselves. The future scientist is a doer and he is anxious to try out a new pattern, a new approach.

This way we discover misunderstandings, missing links which have not been properly stressed. By repetition of the thought process, it is more firmly embedded in his memory and becomes properly "his" to be used at other times in identical or merely similar situations. In the end they become tools of

135

his subconscious, one of his many keys which his subconscious will try on a nagging problem in some other more complicated situation. This intellectual growth the teacher will observe in most serious courses. He sees that his students have grown through the semester. They become more sophisticated, more sure of themselves in mathematical reasoning. And it would be impossible to ignore that even their personality has grown which is the ultimate goal of the educational process.

The special psychological situation of problem solving seems to have much to do with the fear of mathematics, with the notion that mathematics is "difficult." At the earliest age in elementary school the student is assigned problems, where much independent thinking is required, even if only on an elementary level. Facing the new demanding situation alone, all on his own, may be a new, frightening experience. The difficulty may not lie in the student's inability to solve problems, but in this particular psychological situation. If this difficulty is psychological, then it should be also resolved by psychological means. It seems that not enough attention has been paid to that and many losses in our educational setup may be traced to this factor. Too many failures are explained by a lack of talent for mathematics of many students.

The above problems are magnified when we start being interested in promising "gifted" adolescents. I am mainly concerned here with high school students. The National Science Foundation has realized that if we can identify and motivate future productive mathematicians and scientists at the formative period, i.e., from the eighth to the twelfth grade, that we will lose fewer potential scientists, and they will come to the universities better prepared, both scientifically and psychologically.

The first question we faced was to identify the proper individuals. We found that to add to the application of a page of difficult problems which required almost no mathematical background—mathematical puzzles you might call them—was the best means of identification. A six-weeks summer program consisted of lectures on intriguing nonmanipulative subjects which preferably would not be the subjects of later normal course work, and *creative problems*.

It is interesting to note how high in the students' favor these problems score. You can see how the problems catch hold of their imagination, of their subconscious. They try different ideas without success, the old key-and-lock game is used. Suddenly something clicks and they are sure they have the answer. They try to communicate it, their words come in an excited emotional torrent, not being able to keep pace with their ideas. They cannot make themselves clear and they realize that the answer is still beyond their reach. They probably have it, but they still have to dig it out of the subconscious.

Many traits of their character will come into play: ambition, a stubborn energy, competitiveness, the will to prove themselves, etc. These drive their minds towards a solution. Even when they go through their routine every-day activities, there is something inside nagging at them and working on the problem.

Finally, the solution seems to come without any immediate further effort. Sometimes after a rest, sometimes in the morning they seem to see clearer. They feel "they know" but the details necessary for satisfactory communication might still be eluding them. There is more work left to be done to dig it out in its entirety. They start seeing shortcuts. This last period of the reward, the joy of problem solving. The release of an almost unbearable tension. It is an experience which other people might envy the mathematician. This wonderful experience will bring them back to new problems. This is the way to make mathematicians.

Here we have tried to describe the psychological stages of the solution of a particular creative problem. The presence at a summer session of many other gifted mathematicians, all at the same stage, makes their achievement in addition socially significant.

At the end, let us point out sources of creative problems. You find many in the numerous mathematical puzzle books. An infinite variety is in the pages of the *American Mathematical Monthly* which has been devoting much energy to this subject for decades. A special mathematical contest book has been published by the American Mathematical Association. Two volumes of a *Hungarian Problem Book* and a *Russian Problem Book* have been published in the "New Mathematical Library." Other sources have been published, associated with the names *Scientific American, Litton Corporation, The Scientific Supplement of the London Times*, etc.

A B C D E F G H I J K   0 6 9 8 7 6
PRINTED IN THE UNITED STATES OF AMERICA
148CG
148DG